INTERNATIONAL LITERARY FESTIVAL AUTUMN 2002

THE ART

Lecture Theatre
University of
East Anglia

All events begin
at 7pm.

Season Tickets
£30 (Students and
Concessions £18)

Individual Tickets
£5 (Students and
Concessions £3)

Proof of eligibility for
concessions will be
required

Available in advance
from the Box Office,
sited in Union House,
UEA

Open 10am - 5pm
weekdays term time,
12 noon - 3pm
vacations

Telephone: 01603
508050

(Credit and debit card
payments are subject to
a booking fee)

By Post:
Box Office, Union
House, UEA, Norwich
NR4 7TJ

(Cheques payable to:
SUS (E.A.) Ltd.
Please enclose a
stamped addressed
envelope)

KEELY Print

SWALLOW NELSON HOTEL Norwich ★ ★ ★

ADNAMS

WATERSTONE'S
The last word in books

east |arts

UEA NORWICH

Arundhati ROY
The God of Small Things, The Algebra of Infinite Justice
Wednesday October 16

Alan AYCKBOURN
The Norman Conquests, A Chorus of Disapproval, House and Garden
Monday October 21

Donna TARTT
The Secret History, The Little Friend
Monday October 28

Jeremy PAXMAN
The English: A Portrait of a People, Political Animal
Monday November 4

Seamus HEANEY
Beowulf, Electric Light, Finders Keepers
Monday November 11

Thomas KENEALLY
Schindler's Ark, Homebush Boy, The Office of Innocence
Thursday November 14

Harold PINTER
The Caretaker, Betrayal, Celebration
Monday November 18

Number 6 Autumn 2002

Guest Editor: D. J. Taylor
Managing Editor: Katri Skala
Design & Production: Julian p Jackson
Publicity & Events: Sarah Gooderson
Marketing & Subscriptions: Emma Forsberg
Editorial Assistant: Emily Knee

Pretext Editorial Board: Julia Bell, Peter Bush, Jon Cook, Patricia Duncker, Ian McEwan, Andrew Motion, Michele Roberts

Thanks to the following people for making this magazine possible:
The Arts Council of England, the Regional Arts Lottery Programme, Jon Cook and Val Striker at UEA, the Centre for Creative and Performing Arts.

SUBMISSIONS: *Pretext* is published twice a year, in May and in November. Deadline for May issue is end of January, deadline for November issue is end of July. We do not acknowledge submissions, and due to the volume of material, it may take up to five months to hear back from us. If you wish to have your work returned, please enclose a SAE. For more detailed submission guidelines please turn to pages 139-140.

TO SUBSCRIBE: call 01603 592783 or e-mail info@penandinc.co.uk. One year subscription for individuals (two issues) costs £14 (UK), £16.50 (rest of world), for institutions £18 (UK), £22 (rest of world). Or visit our website<http://www.penandinc.co.uk>

Pretext is published by Pen&inc, English and American Studies, University of East Anglia and distributed by Central Books, 99 Wallace Rd, London, E9 5LN

ISBN: 1-902913-15-9

Printed and bound by Biddles Ltd, Woodbridge Park, Guildford.

BRITISH CENTRE FOR LITERARY TRANSLATION

Promoting literature in translation through workshops, readings, publications and research

*In*Other *Words*: The journal for literary translators and anyone interested in good writing and the creative process.

NO. 19 – CHILDREN'S LITERATURE SPECIAL ISSUE – NOW AVAILABLE
NO. 20 – WINTER 2002 – AVAILABLE DECEMBER

Free inspection copy of *In*Other *Words* and more information about BCLT activities from:

Catherine Fuller
Co-ordinator, British Centre for Literary Translation
School of English and American Studies
University of East Anglia
Norwich
NR4 7TJ

email: bclt@uea.ac.uk
www.literarytranslation.com

Contents

PUNK OF ME

Its all been very punk of me
and how . . .
it's all been very punk of me
oh, punk of me

Punk of me
punk of me

Punk of me
a little porcelain
a little arch
a little dog in the rain

Punk of me
punk of me

Stretched to an unsavoury limit
like Ozzy Osbourne and Dmitri Shostakovich

Punk of me
punk of me

– 2001, Howard Devoto

D. J. Taylor
Introduction

Two significant literary events took place in the first week of September 2002. One was the arrival in the bookshops of Zadie Smith's second novel, *The Autograph Man*. The other was the death, at the ripe age of 92, of the novelist William Cooper. And their respective treatments? Ms Smith found herself profiled in three weekend newspapers, divulged details of her kitchen to the *Sunday Times* 'Living' supplement and the attractions of her writer's retreat to the *Sunday Telegraph*. William Cooper, without whose *Scenes From Provincial Life* (1950) post-war Eng. lit. would have followed a markedly different track, got a single decent obituary. Standing in a pew at his funeral ten days later and discreetly reckoning up the number of mourners – there were sixteen of us – I deduced that there was a moral here somewhere.

The moral, alas, was that elemental one about most of the public interest occasionally stirred up in literature having an essentially non-literary cause. The *Evening Standard*, which started the whole Zadie Smith bandwagon rolling, doesn't care about the merits, or otherwise, of *The Autograph Man*. It is simply that its author – young, bright, 'ethnic' – is irresistible. One can think of half-a-dozen youngish novelists – Jeanette Winterson, Will Self, Irvine Welsh – whose personalities and the presentation of them are entirely separable from the things they write. Nothing new about this, of course – the ground-down hacks in *New Grub Street*, George Gissing's doomy novel of late-Victorian literary life, were lamenting it over a century ago – and from the angle of literature scarcely worth bothering about. That there may be better books than *The Autograph Man* published this

Introduction

year isn't perhaps the point. Ms Smith is the future of the English novel, you see, even – or rather especially – to people who barely know that the English novel exists.

This is not a complaint about Zadie Smith, who seems to have handled a media frenzy not of her making with enviable decorum. But the effect of the Smith phenomenon, and others like it, is inevitably to reduce yet further the exposure allowed to people who fall short of the specification now demanded by newspapers of an 'interesting writer'. In a book world dominated by a handful of publishing firms and a handful of chain retailers, the margins – that tiny space harbouring the kind of books that are worth taking seriously – are becoming, well, more marginal, more fenced off and disregarded by the mainstream taste and the pundits who form it. Several of the non-fiction pieces assembled here reflect, either directly or indirectly, on this dilemma, which might be baldly stated as: how to see that proper attention is paid to good novels when the public's idea of a good novel is Joanna Trollope. Some of the stories, I hope, are examples of it – work for which there is hardly room outside the pages of specialist and subsidised literary magazines.

As for guiding principles, the only one which springs to mind is that of offering a glance or two at the kind of contemporary writing that exists in this country beyond the orbit of the broadsheet profile, the Waterstone's check-list and the literary prize garland, the things that you wouldn't know were there unless you looked. For it is a fact that much of what is worthwhile in modern English literary life goes on almost un-noticed, a kind of low-level subterranean existence played out far away from the high street window displays and the literary festivals. Rather like the passing of William Cooper, to whose memory what follows is dedicated.

D.J. Taylor
Norwich, 2002

Annie Murray
Eggshells

I went egg-picking for the Wylies most days that summer. It was 1972 and I was ten.

Although the farm was never called anything but 'Wylies' then, its proper name was Castle Farm. In the Middle Ages much of its land lay within the castle walls which extended high and forbidding along the river, but the castle has been a ruin for centuries now, pale corners of it dotted among the grazing dairy herd like eccentric sculptures.

The farm was not far from town, up an ankle-turning track. We fetched our eggs from the Wylies, and milk which you could still get by the jug. Mrs Wylie stood in her apron at the door opposite the milking sheds, ginger-haired, slow-moving, speaking only when circumstances demanded. That year she usually had baby Trevor clasped snivelling on one hip, while she moved back and forth to the kitchen table where the eggs were piled in their grey boxes.

I suppose Jane Wylie was depressed. Then, I thought of most grown-ups as weary, dulled by the sheer condition of adulthood. I didn't see, with her, that it was something other than tiredness: more a kind of absence. She never interested me. I was a tomboy, scornful of the sort of things women did indoors. The farm was otherwise a vigorous, outdoor place on which I was hooked, and awoke each day itching to be there.

Alan Wylie was a mountain of a man, full of muscular energy. He wore his shirtsleeves rolled and black trousers tucked into giant welly boots. They had two older boys. Colin was fourteen. I never found him interesting either: he was pale, red-haired, and unlike the rest of his fleshy family, had the stunted look of a child nourished on split peas and swede, a throwback to the days of *Piers Plowman*. Neil was my friend. He was a just a couple of months older than me, wide-faced with pudding-basin black hair and a smile so broad and eye-narrowing it made him look Chinese. We were in tune to perfection that summer. I loved his country accent, his zest for everything. I have a picture of him in my mind, an eternal representation: Neil tearing across the cow-dung surface of the yard with the dogs, Jessie and Mac, a grin showing his big teeth, and bursting with schemes. 'Come on Sal – let's build a camp!' Or go fishing, or for a bike ride.

We buried my father last week, and as the only child it falls to me to stay and settle things, to dispose of decades of careful, waste-conscious hoarding. Since I live abroad, none of it is of use to me.

Our home was over a hardware shop in a side street. Dad was a busy, anxious man, who seemed always to be in the shop in holland overalls among the nails and galvanized buckets. He never did retire, a heart attack transferring him, at seventy-two, from the shop to the hospital Mum died in 1987. She was rather fragile, took in sewing and suffered from migraines. They were loving but preoccupied and it felt a shadowy life we led. I went to a school in another town, so my friends were scattered round the villages, but at ten I was allowed to join in the egg-picking at weekends. By that besotted summer, Neil and I were inseparable.

We did our egg-picking together. The henhouses were on the river side of the milking sheds and you could hear the chickens before you got inside.

When we pushed the metal trolley stacked with collecting trays through the door, the birds in the nearest cages would go quiet. The sheds were dark, lit when necessary by dim electric lights, and they smelled of the hens' mealy food, raw egg, sour chicken droppings. At the far end, where it was darkest, cobwebs furred with dust sagged across corners.

There were four aisles of battery pens with sloping racks beneath, into which the eggs rolled. Sudden noises made the hens go quiet, but other signs of goings-on in their otherwise wing-cramped existence could rev them up into a cacophony of clucking. Neil and I experimented with a variety of chicken sound effects while trawling for handfuls of warm eggs.

'Helicopter!' Neil might cry, charging the aisle, arms whirling.

'Jack-in-the-box!' And I'd creep along, squatting, then star jump up in front of the cages. The effect was like turning the volume dial of a radio up and down. How we laughed.

The eggs kept on coming and coming. The chickens watched severely out of red-rimmed eyes as we stole their children. Sometimes we'd drop one, leaving on the ground a slime of yellow and shell. And occasionally one of us would shriek –

'Ugh, look! One of these!'

An egg which lay there looking like the others, but when you went to pick it up you found it had no shell, just the soft, unnerving membrane, jelloid in your hand. Neil once managed to draw a blue blob on one with a felt pen and pretend it was an eyeball.

After the collecting came grading. The eggs had to be lined up on a narrow conveyor belt. They were fed along the grader and rolled off, according to size, down a rubber covered slope divided up by little wooden partitions. As they gathered at the bottom we transferred them into egg boxes marked with their grade. It was fast work. The heaviest eggs rolled off into the first compartment, a select few size 1s, gigantic and pale, the shell often ridged by the chicken's straining. Hordes of them tumbled off at sizes 2, 3 and 4, white, brown, speckled, sometimes with a tiny fluff of feather stuck to them, occasionally cracked, fit only for the tray of discards and misfits. The numbers tailed off with the diminutive 5s, and finally came the freak, bouncy-ball sized 6s and 7s. Once we found one like a large marble, treacly brown.

I liked to rush back and forth, packing eggs at frantic speed, fuelled by a 'please notice me' adoration of Alan Wylie. And unlike my own father, he did notice. Sometimes Colin was there, and other kids earning a half crown (despite decimalization). But he always found a word for me.

'Keep it up young Sally – you're one of my best workers . . .' He'd call across the grader. Often his eyes were waiting when I looked up, and a chirpy smile. He might tickle me under the arms when he passed. 'Oops – don't drop any!' as I buckled, giggling.

Gradually over that summer he showed me things on the farm. In the milking shed he pushed my fingers into the slots where the cows' teats went, to feel the machine's weird, sucking pull. Sometimes he scooped me on to his shoulders to take me to the house for the treats, hands on my skinny ankles and I'd laugh, excited, queening it over Neil from on high.

Treats came after grading, before the tea-time milking. So far as I can make out Alan Wylie must have bought the things we ate himself. He certainly orchestrated these beanfeasts, sitting us on the strip of grass in front of the house. He'd produce Corona Limeade in dazzling green, bowls of Sherbet Lemons and Liquorice Allsorts, Milky Ways and Mar Bars to cut up for whoever was there. His own blue and white striped mug held at least a pint of tea and he'd stand leaning against the door frame, drink in one hand, stroking his beard with the other as we guzzled sweets. He made sure our cups were full.

'Come on Sal – course you can manage another drop. It'll be flat by tomorrow.' He was like one long party. He cajoled us to eat until our stomachs lurched with sweetness. Sometimes he played with us, throwing me over his head until I nearly sicked with laughter.

Jane Wylie was usually inside. She'd look up mildly as we appeared for treats. She wore a flowery apron and was nearly always ironing or feeding a shrieking Trevor.

Except once. I came up to the farm one boiling hot afternoon. Boats were sliding back and forth along the river, between the bright willows. I was looking for Neil but no one seemed to be about and I wandered round the end of the house where a side window looked into their living room. In the still afternoon a fly smacked up against the pane, then buzzed heavily away. Inside, I saw Jane Wylie. She didn't have her apron on, just enormous white shorts and a baby pink T-shirt, tight enough to show the roll of fat above her waist. She'd pushed the chairs back and was dancing barefoot to some smooth music. It wasn't any particular dance. She stood on one slabby leg, the other swinging out straight, toes pointed. Her arms were curved out in front as if she was embracing a partner and she skipped and twirled. It made me feel nasty inside. She looked dreadful, like a fat fairy with curly red hair. What on earth was she doing?

4

Why didn't the stupid woman get out into the warm day, like the men?

I saw Colin Wylie this morning. It was a shock, catching sight of one of them. I'd assumed they'd moved away, wouldn't have come near this town again. Market day still sets up on a Wednesday, even after all these years, across the square from the Town Hall. I saw Colin's pale, root vegetable face sideways on as he dropped spring cabbage into a carrier bag and hung it on the buggy next to him. In it was a freckly toddler in a sun hat. An older boy stood alongside. So Colin's a father, I thought. He'd be forty-three now. God knows, I hope he's happy. Last time I saw him was the week before he and Neil were taken to the children's home in Didcot.

Thirty years ago, Neil and I had bicycles and rode through this square, as well as bumping along field tracks with the dogs, cows watching us, rock still. We built a camp behind the henhouses, went to the river where the big lads larked about, jumping like human water bombs off the road bridge. We played in the old ARP bunker tucked between the trees. Alan Wylie built us a go-kart. I watched his huge hands fix the axle, thighs like vast continents to me as he squatted in the yard. That afternoon Jane Wylie ventured out with a tray of orange squash and Ritz biscuits. Her husband stared up at her for a moment, but didn't speak or smile.

In the heat of August Bank Holiday, Neil took sick. He lay sweaty in bed, spewing yellow bile. The other kids' families had gone to the coast, but not mine. Mum had one of her heads.

'I'll do the collecting!' I told Alan Wylie, fidgeting with importance. 'I can do it all!'

I started at the side, the narrowest part: hens on my right, wall to my left. I hadn't collected on my own before – it was always Neil and me. The lights weren't on as it was a bright day, and a little daylight filtered in through the small window. The henhouse felt eerie, deep in shadow at the far end. I didn't like the look of it, but I'd said I'd do it. I'd show him I could! He had the power to make me feel big and grand.

Pushing the trolley further along, I grabbed eggs, two per hand. It was a still afternoon and the farm felt so quiet outside. I got more scared. I didn't know what I was frightened of but the follicles at the back of my neck began to tingle. Gradually, I started to need to pee, but I pressed on, fighting my unease. My arms goose-bumped. All the strings of my body played one tune – run, run! But I was going to stay 'til I'd finished. By the time I got down to the end my need was so great I was hopping from foot to foot, but I didn't want to stop collecting. It was dark here – no one would know, would they? . . . I yanked my shorts down to my knees and squatted, gushing between my legs. Doing up the zip, I turned, but the way back was blocked. I jumped, like a spasm going through me and a last trickle of hot wee went into my knickers. I hadn't heard Alan Wylie come in. My cheeks burned. He must have seen! He was a little way along the shadowy aisle, leaning with one elbow against the wall, watching, hand slowly stroking his beard. For once he wasn't smiling, but stern, a trick of light making him into someone else. Then the smile crept back.

'Getting on all right, pet?'

'Yes –' My legs were shaking, but his burring accent made things normal again. 'I've done loads – look!'

'You're a good girl. Pity about Neil today.'

He helped me then, and when the collecting was done, he gave me a whole Mars Bar for myself and watched me eat it in the yard.

The week before school was due to start was still sultry, the air full of jazzing gnats and floating bits. Dandelion clocks puffed seeds silently to the breeze.

Neil and I went to the river with the dogs that afternoon. Close to the bridge were little beaches where the bank had been scraped out. We paddled and swam in the slow moving shallows, screaming with excitement when the wake of boats swelled the brown water to waves, rocking the moorhens. Shrieks came from the paddling pool on the other side of the bridge. As the afternoon waned and the sun became a failing fireball, the smell of chips hung in the air. Colin came down too, and for the first time ever, mouth yanked into a rictus of alarm, jumped writhing from the bridge into the deep middle of the current.

The dogs were with us and Neil and I found sticks for them. Neil wore only shorts, tight on him, his chest and back tanned a rich brown.

'Go on, girl!' He kept calling to Jessie, trailing a stick in temptation past her snout. 'In you go!' Mac, the terrier, charged in after every throw, little legs driving gamely against the water, bringing back sticks longer than his own body. Lady-like Jessie yapped, advancing and retreating at the water's edge. Neil and I waded in and whistled her, but she wouldn't come.

Neil had some Wrigleys Juicy Fruit and we squatted on the beach.

'Two for you –' He handed the yellow-wrapped sticks over. 'Two for me . . . better leave that one for Colin . . .'

As we stood up, chewing, we saw her, Jane Wylie in the wrong place, running, Trevor in her arms. For a moment I couldn't take in that she'd come all the way along the track, across the road bridge, down to the water. She was wearing sheepskin slippers.

'Boys!' It was the only time I'd ever heard her shriek. 'You've got to come 'ome – *now*.'

She didn't tell me not to go with them, so I just followed. The farm was deserted when we got there. No one did the milking that afternoon. Mrs Wylie set Trevor down at the kitchen table and only then, saw me. She went mad, throwing her heavy body from side to side, screaming.

'What're you doing 'ere? Get away from 'ere, now!'

No one said anything to stop her. Colin and Neil just stood, completely bewildered. That was what hurt most at the time, Neil not sticking up for me. I tore down the track, grief a hard ache in my throat, though I didn't know what all the upset was about, not for a long time.

After it happened my mother said it was a great pity the Wylies had to move so suddenly, that I wasn't to worry about it – I must turn more to my school friends. For a time conversations would stop when I walked into rooms and then the subject died. But nothing felt right to me for much longer: the fields and the river were haunted.

I travelled a lot after leaving school. For years I taught in Spain and settled in my husband's native city, Salamanca. Our daughters are bilingual. This time, coming back here to our town, I see the farm has gone. It was sold, back in the 1970s, became 'Castle

Farm' again and stayed looking the same for many years. Now, they've built a block of high-grade apartments on the site, facing the river. Where the cows used to line up for milking is a posh entrance lodge and there are expensive cars parked outside. It's very quiet, no distant skirl of hens now, no smells.

Mum told me, finally, before she died. She even had clippings still, from *The Herald*. Alan Wylie pleaded 'not guilty,' but the courts knew better and he was sent down for five years. Even the police claimed to be shocked by the case.

Jane Wylie had a long spell in the Fairmile, the local psychiatric hospital, and all three boys were taken into care. I never wrote to Neil after he left. Now, I feel ashamed of that, but I was only ten and thought I'd been rejected. I've never asked what happened to Alan Wylie later on, or to the two girls. The first one lived in a village ten miles away, but the second girl was local. Her father found her that night, after she'd managed to crawl half way home from the Croft, a scrubby remnant of land on the far edge of town. Both girls were in their early teens, not a handful of years older than me. Even now I struggle to put together the Alan Wylie of fizzy limeade with the one in the court reports and feel betrayed by the unreliability of appearances, constantly alert for an egg that has no shell.

I do wonder about Neil, and little Trevor. But this morning, at the market, my feet wouldn't move one inexorably after the other towards Colin Wylie, to greet, remind. To force us both back into the smoke of youthful pain.

I turned away until he and his children had passed and wandered the market stalls selecting cheese, salad, eggs. Tapped each of the shells. Just to be sure.

Alan Jenkins
Two Poems

THE CLASSICAL PICNIC

To pass through an arched gate and a shady arbour
From the Terrace garden
And its sternly ordered rose-beds, barbered lawns – barely
A distance of two paces –
Was to enter a different world entirely.
My arm around her waist would guide her
Towards a riot of nettles, buttercups, wild grasses:
After the narrow straits of deckchairs
It felt like coming into harbour.
We knew it only as The Meadow,
Though it had other names among the locals,
Distressed gentlefolk and old-age pensioners
Who gazed at lily-ponds and fountains from their benches.
Our loitering steps slowed to a standstill
And then we'd sink together in some shadow.
Inevitably, she'd help everything to harden
And I'd slide one finger, two, inside her.

The Classical Picnic

Thistles grew there, and midges in cloud-clusters
Swarmed to us, and we were sometimes flustered
By the proximity of other couples
Who found the same use for the place as we did,
Oblivious to that snake in the grass, the river
As it glinted away into the valley;
Some walked their dogs there, and the odd voyeur
Prowled around until he got an eyeful.
What did it matter, as long as we could lie together?
And once, believing in our carnal innocence
That all this hot fumbling made us grown-ups,
We decided to act as grown-ups seemed to,
Pretending that the pleasure we knew awaited
Was not the purpose of our outing,
And took food and drink, which we spread on a blanket –

There's even garlands for you, violet wreaths and saffron,
And lilies plucked where they grow by the virgin river,
And little cheeses that they dry in baskets of rushes,
And plums that ripen in the autumn weather,
And chestnuts, and the cheerful red of apples.
In brief, here's Ceres, love, and rowdy Bacchus –
And red-stained blackberries, and grapes in bunches,
And hanging from his frame, sea-green cucumber.
And here's the little god who keeps the arbour,
Fierce with his sickle and enormous belly . . .

You be damned, you with your Puritan eyebrows!
What thanks will cold ashes give for the sweetness of garlands?
Or do you intend to hang a rose-wreath on your tombstone?
Set down the wine and the dice and perish who thinks of tomorrow!
Here's death twitching my ear: 'Live,' says he, 'for I'm coming.'

CHRIST IN THE OLIVE GROVE
after Gérard de Nerval †

When our Lord, seized by the poet's fine frenzy,
lifted up his skinny arms beneath the holy trees
and had been long lost to speechless miseries,
and believed himself betrayed by ungrateful friends,

he turned to those who were waiting for him down below,
who dreamt of being prophets, sages, kings
but were bloated, dull, and slept like bestial things
and he cried out: 'God does not exist! It's all blah!'

They slumbered on. 'Friends! Haven't you heard the newsflash?
My head has touched the everlasting vault;
bleeding, broken, I've suffered all the ills of the flesh!

Brothers, I lied: there's no shortage of void! From the altar
where I'm the sacrifice, He's given us the slip –
no God, no God any more!' Somehow they stayed asleep . . .

'Everything's dead' – He took up the theme again.
'I've lost my flight-path among the stars,
I've gone through worlds, ranged as widely and as far
as the sand or sea that pours through fecund veins –

desert sands, heaving oceans, whirlpools, waves . . .
A tenuous breath blows the vagrant planets, but no mind
moves anywhere on that vastness. I tried to find
the eye of God: bottomless black socket, caves

of chaos and old night, nothingness, the vortex, the pit . . .
Cold Necessity that rules dead worlds, permafrost,
colliding burnt-out suns: do we know you haven't lost it?

---

† Gérard de Nerval (1808-1855), French poet whose work included *La Bohème Galante* (1855) and *Le Rêve et la vie* (1855). 'Christ in the Olive Grove' is adapted from *Les Chimères*, a sequence of twelve sonnets, which were appended to *Les Filles du feu* (1854), a book of tales.

Christ in the Olive Grove

My father! Are you there in me? Do you still have power
over life and death? Or did a dark angel get you first?
I sense that I'm alone – alone and weeping, and my hour
is at hand . . . If I go, everything goes!'
                                    But no one heard him,
moaning, pouring his over-burdened heart out,
almost done for, the eternal sacrificial victim.
He called the one person who was up and about

in all Jerusalem: 'Judas,' he cried, 'You know what I'm
likely to fetch – why don't you make a quick sale
and shut up shop before I'm stretched out in the hail . . .
You who have the strength and conviction of your crime!'

But Judas took himself off, moodily, to rue
how little he ever got paid, and construe
his own black nature in the writing on the wall –

his conscience was biting him so hard . . .
In the end, Pilate, Caesar's eyes, took pity and called
'Go find me this madman!' to the guard.

John Murray
Making a Killing

Regional versus Metropolitan Writing

A re writers out there in the regions eclipsed and marginalized, swindled and denied the limelight, by those in the capital? If you are stuck three or four hundred miles from all the publishers and agents and literary shindigs and opportunities to network and grovel, are you seriously one down before you start? Is there really a Literary Mafia-inspired surfeit of fiction about Belsize Park, ciabatta bread and serial adultery? Also, why is there that hoary old publisher's gag that goes, 'I'm a little bit worried. *I've just bought ten first novels, and they're all set in Halifax'*?

I believe that there is a great deal of misconception and bogus conflation when it comes to discussion about metropolitan versus provincial writing. It is not only a misleading antithesis, but it distracts from much more important issues such as, is this writer any good or not regardless of where they come from? After all, it doesn't take a great deal of research to see that all the way through the twentieth century there were periods when certain kinds of regional fiction exerted an enormous and uncanny influence. My view is that these regional fads and crazes were by and large publisher- (i.e. metropolis-) inspired, and for whatever reason it has frequently pushed certain regional writers to write to expectation and be marketed accordingly. For example: urban dereliction, heroin abuse, and even serial killing country-style(all mediated via quirkily articulate narrators, often steeped in amateur sociology, folk psychology, street philosophy et cetera) are a highly bankable feature of the current regional writing scene. This smooth and profitable collusion between successful regional writer and delighted London publisher has distorted what I would call the *nuanced* and really interesting reality of the region concerned. In doing so it has often prevented an original and versatile artistic exploration of what it really means to live and breathe in, say, Glasgow, Workington, Fife, Merthyr Tydfil, Ballymena, or the Isle of Muck.

I will say more about this artistic distortion later, but in the meantime if you want to talk some crude literary sociology, here are a few things to mull over whether you live in Brent Cross or Bolsover. In 1985 I spoke to the Literature Officer of a Regional Arts Association covering a wealthy part of the London commuter belt. Her total annual budget which also had to pay her salary was £20, 000. At the same time Northern Arts which then covered the North East and Cumbria gave more than that sum to just one of its numerous clients, namely Neil Astley's Bloodaxe Books. The impoverished London-overspill body could not support a single literary magazine much less a distinguished publishing house. Fast forward a decade to 1995 and you would have found Northern Arts alone subsidizing, I would guess, about three-quarters of the best-regarded fiction outlets across the whole of the UK. *Stand*, *Writing Women*, *Iron* and *Panurge* were all funded by a single regional authority. Much the same applies at the time of writing. If, in 2002, you are a writer who wants access to bursaries, grants, residencies, and now even an agency purpose-built to look after your work, your publishing and your money interests (New Writing North) you should go and settle in Morpeth or Alnwick or Haltwhistle, not in poor old beggarly and antediluvian Hampstead.

The problem is that crude literary sociology is not the main concern of fiction readers and certainly not of literary posterity. We don't really care how many bursaries and residencies and literary beanfeasts a writer clocks up, we only care about his or her books and whether they are any good. This is where we come to a new and necessary slant on the business of regional writing, the real and the half real and the ersatz, and how things might be made different. Before I go on to that, however, and to aid me in making a few remedial suggestions, I need to make an excursus and tell you about the time I went down to London to sort them all out and tell them exactly how it should be done . . .

Towards the end of 1997 I left my North Cumbrian farmhouse to make one of my rare trips down to the capital. I had been invited by the Literature Department of the Arts Council to give my considered views about British literary magazines and fiction publishing generally. As founding editor of *Panurge*, which had folded the year before, it was felt that my brains might be worth picking. Edited for six years by David Almond and another six years by me, this Cumbrian magazine had surprised a great many people by what it had achieved. By the late 1980s it had earned a singular reputation for printing outstanding fiction by unknown and emergent writers (Patrick McCabe, Richard Beard and Julia Darling appeared there long before they published any novels.) By the mid-1990s, things were so bad for short story writers, we were even getting submissions from top London agents. Their ten per cent commissions, had we ever accepted these stories, would have amounted to about three or four quid. Memorably, we once turned down a third rate (agented) story by Fay Weldon in favour of a first rate one by an unknown nineteen-year-old. And perplexingly enough all this hard and fast stuff was done in an area better known for its orange anoraks and rum butter teas than for trenchant literary publishing.

I went down there with one or two modest proposals. The first one was that the Arts Council and for that matter all the Regional Arts Associations including Northern Arts should stop subsidizing nearly all the magazines they supported. Most literary magazines I argued, especially the ones that published fiction, articles and reviews, were indifferently edited, appallingly designed and above all excruciatingly boring. Many of them were either slyly or overtly corrupt and operated on the daring 3F principle: they stuffed their pages with work solicited either from the *famous*, the *fashionable* or their *friends*. The ones that couldn't afford to do that were regularly edited by very amiable, very pleasant people who, when it came to intelligent rigour, would have made ideal plumbers or market gardeners. The facts spoke for themselves; most new mags lasted a couple of years at most; their shop sales were negligible because they were designed like bus timetables, often having something like Issue 8, Spring 1996 slapped in 36 point bold on the cover, a sure deterrent to anyone chancing across it in the summer of the same year.

My argument was that literary magazines by 1997 were at best a romantic anachronism and at worst a fatuous distraction from the real problem. Long ago they certainly helped DH Lawrence and Jean Rhys break into print, and even as late as the 1970s Ian McEwan and Adam Mars-Jones found their publishers via the *New Review* and *Quarto*. But in both those periods there was also a vigorous and heterogeneous publishing culture where profit and marketability were not the be all and end all and where the WH Smith computerized till returns did not inevitably determine whether a writer's next book would be taken or not. By 1997 those neither superstars nor bankable first novelists were being unceremoniously booted out by Cape and Secker. Occasionally they were told they were simply too old or not handsome enough to give the book that vital photoshoot push. Even some of the few remaining small independent publishers were coolly threatening their authors with, *Remember, you're only as good as your next book!* Highly talented new writers and highly talented old writers who could not fit the convergent requirements of the new conglomerates were finding it virtually impossible to get published.

So, I argued, instead of wasting resources on literary magazines that nobody read or certainly never read without yawning, funding bodies would be better employed in supporting fiction publishing proper. They did some of this already but they should be doing a hell of a lot more of it, and in fact see it as their *raison d'etre*. Surely the most important thing for the well-being of literature was not the appointment of an exciting new literary fellow at Newcastle or Dundee University, nor an exciting new literary magazine called *Slash*, but the book length publication and dissemination of really outstanding writing by really outstanding writers. This was self-evidently a moral as well as a financial enterprise, though the two were certainly not mutually exclusive.

I have to point out that the two very nice officials I talked to hurriedly scribbled down everything I said as if I was the Legendary Bearded Oracle from the Far North West. I had no easy answers to the fiction crisis but at least I had one or two ideas. I suggested approaching some of the independent publishers they supported already, say Carcanet and Dedalus, and offering them inducements to expand their fiction lists and ease the overall congestion. Pay them, bribe them, to print more first novels, more novels by those who had lost their publishers, more collections of quality short stories. It would all have to be monitored by some sort of funding panel just in case these publishers absent-mindedly siphoned it off for pet projects or translations. At the time I did not mention Gary Pulsifer's *Arcadia* which now seems to me to be a model of its kind. First novels, reissued novels, abandoned British writers brought back from the brink . . . and Gary Pulsifer is not even British, he's an energetic American with our literary interests at heart.

Sad to say, and despite the fact I'd travelled all that way, they took no notice of my modest proposals. Five years later serious fiction publishing is still in the main a laissez-faire like it or lump it joke. However, this joke is part of an interconnected and triangular problem. I believe that if we were to confront any of the three strangulation factors: the conglomerate publishing monopolies, the deliberate publisher-driven homogenisation of 'regional fiction', and the complacently reductive concerns of much non-regional fiction, that all three of these vortices might be realigned for the benefit of all.

But from the general to the particular. What do the following writers all have in common? Mary Webb, Eden Phillpotts, JC and TF Powys, Alan Sillitoe, Stan Barstow, Irvine Welsh, James Kelman, Niall Griffiths, Patrick McCabe, Alan Warner? Well, apart from the fact they are nearly all men, (Discuss. Is 'provincial' writing of the highly successful variety, a largely male pursuit?) they are all examples of current or one-time acclaimed regionalists. The first four all went in for a kind of highly stylized 1920s West Country Gothic. All of them wrote at least one enduring and significant book, as well as a great many awful ones. None of them were sons or daughters of the soil yet they chose to make whimsical atmospheric rusticity their fictional specialism. Despite their obvious unevenness and the ease with which Stella Gibbons could parody them, they were all at various times, especially by their publishers, ludicrously compared to Thomas Hardy. No need to labour the point, but whatever Hardy was guilty of, he was scarcely guilty of whimsy: he went in for austere drama not purple melodrama, and his tragedies were genuinely tragic. His characters were soaked in and inseparable from their Wessex environment, but they were not soaked to the point of putrefaction.

Jump three or four decades to the late 1950s and early 1960s. Here we find Gritty Northern Realism from the likes of Barstow, Braine, Sillitoe and Shelagh Delaney. It might seem like old hat now but many of their bestselling novels were successfully filmed and they all made a dizzy income for a time. It was hardly their fault, but they canonized the set requirements, the accepted poetics of 'the northern novel', for a considerable period. If this sounds like exaggeration, I can assure you that for decades, certainly well into the mid-1980s, the staple drama from the BBC Leeds and Manchester studios, as broadcast on Radios 3 and 4, was undiluted northern grit. Even now it still exerts its curiously analgesic presence in some young as well as old northern novelists. The trouble was not only was it not really gritty, it was not really northern, and it was not really real. If you doubt this assertion take out your copy of Barstow's classic, *A Kind of Loving*. The only really abrasive stuff here, the best and very fleeting thing in the book, is Vic getting drunk and puking up over his hideous mother-in-law. Now look at the early chapters and read Vic's depiction of his own family, especially his mother. Soft-centred, sentimentally woven, nebulous to the point of non-existence. She is not a genuine evocation of someone credibly from Barstow's Wakefield, she is an artless bit of wish-fulfilment.

Perhaps this is starting to look like a mean-spirited and treacherous demolition job by a disgruntled and very envious regional obscurity. So two things need stressing at this point. All the writers on that list, from Mary Webb through to Alan Warner, have a definite and estimable talent. It is just that their influence and their prominence are incommensurate with the originality of that talent. There is clearly nothing unjust when well written novels about Glasgow and Edinburgh derelicts and junkies receive their due accolades. But given that the star Caledonian turns before Kelman and Welsh were Muriel Spark, and before her Eric Linklater and Lewis Grassic Gibbon, we are entitled to ask ourselves how come this new canon is not only so radically other, but also so masonically exclusive? Believe you me I'm not, I swear, pining for an atmospheric Highland or Lowland laddie in the shape of a new Neil Munro or a new Laird of Abbotsford. But is there, I ask myself, a cat in hell's chance that a brilliantly written family saga or an infinitely subtle novel of manners from Dumfries or Dalbeattie would ever get a yes from a London publisher? Even if that same novel happened to be soaked to the bone in the inimitable flavour of backstreet Dumfries, so that the spirit of the Queen of the South was realer to us than the taste of our Belsize Park ciabatta bread, would we stricken London publishers finally be ineluctably shamed into printing *a really great and enduring regional novel . . . but which had no obvious marketing angle apropos the Scottish writing that sells?*

I had great hopes when a young Scots writer from Oban came along. I know Oban and the Western Isles very well and I didn't care whether this writer's genius expressed itself in the guise of Gritty Oban Realism, Magic Oban Realism, an Oban verse novel or *ein echt Obanischer Bildungsroman.* I was looking forward tremendously to being soaked in Obanness and Obanity. But talented as Alan Warner is, his books do not haunt me with the particularity, the thusness of his home town. In his 1998 novel, *The Sopranos*, he portrays a bunch of effervescent streetwise Oban lassies on a charabanc trip to the big city. Yet, strange to say, if you were to take away the odd 'aye' or 'och' or 'dinnae' from this largely dialogue-driven novel, they could just as well be identikit representatives of outer Dagenham or Welwyn Garden City. As for the narrative, Warner's style and syntax, I would say, are more suggestive of trailer park USA (Dirty Realism circa 1986, when Warner was 22) than they are of an Argyll seaport. Note that I am certainly not pleading for any long descriptive passages, or a faultless documentary ear for the pub dialogue of Oban satellite towns like Crianlarich or Tobermory. I am not even pleading for Warner to be any different from the way God made him. What I am saying is that if someone else from the Oban area wrote a multifaceted regional masterpiece that *really* brought the place to life in an enduring work of art, because it was not at all Warneresque, it would never find a publisher.

Making a Killing

No need to push it much further. Just to ask why two of our most prominent Celtic talents, Niall Griffiths and Patrick McCabe, both publish novels in 2001 (*Sheepshagger* and *Emerald Germs of Ireland*) where both protagonists, are, wait for it, *rustic serial killers*. Parenthetically, and it might have something to do with the fact Griffiths is actually from Liverpool, his Aberystwyth area dialogue reads about as indelibly Welsh as it does Old Church Slavonic. Meanwhile some forty per cent of Patrick McCabe's acclaimed novels (two out of five) have heroes who are rustic serial killers. They are both inhabitants of small town Monaghan and they are both compulsive serial killers. Pat, I know fiction isn't meant to be like real life, but even within its own imaginative terms can we really believe in this surreal profusion of South Ulster psychopathy? Are R.S.K's a surefire bankable fictional feature, and especially if you are being chivvied about the sales of your last one? But given that in the same year, even Salman Rushdie gets in on the act with an exiled urban serial killer and a professor to boot, perhaps they can be excused.

My own version of regional fiction is unfortunately very much my own, and it has not made me rich, or even faintly visible. I try to represent my native Cumbria through tongue in cheek multiple narratives, comic exaggeration and manic linguistic play, all bona fide artistic strategies given that the indigenous dialect literature, the Cummerlan Tyal, has been doing all of that for at least a hundred years. I am also much influenced by European literary models: I often feel more in fictional common with comic East Europeans such as Bohumil Hrabal than I do with, say, contemporary northern regionalists. In a nutshell, and preposterous as it sounds, I think tale-spinning Hrabal has more to say about the subtle, authentic spirit of Cumbria than one or two of its homegrown literary apologists. I have received some very generous critical acclaim for my half dozen books, but the metropolitan publishers will not touch me with a bargepole. I promise you I am not bellyaching or sulking at this point, because in many ways I am happy to be with a small independent press where in lieu of money I am given a great deal of pampering and personal attention. The thing is I believe there must be a fair few conspicuously talented regional writers who do not conform to their predicated regional mould, and who therefore languish on the publishing sidelines, or perhaps just give up ever trying to get in print. To return to my threefold argument, I think the same is true for certain highly original and highly talented non-regionalists, especially if they are too old, too ugly, or they prefer to use two or three adjectives where their dazzling twenty-three-year-old editor thinks that one or even none would be perfectly adequate.

image: windfarm - gregg potter
<greggpotter@btopenworld.com>

Charlie Boxer
A Tale of the Republic

To the town's antiquarian, twelve years younger than me though he was, I would listen politely, except when he began on his new topic of ethnology. To hear him repeat his travellers' tales, sifted and categorized into specious theory, gave me the fiercest moments of indignation I ever knew.

I know nothing, but that is more than him. Once, rather than walk away, I interrupted: 'Why don't you talk about something interesting? Why don't you learn about something we can trust you on?'

'Like what?' he smiled.

'Like all the things about us we never hear talked about,' I said. 'For instance,' and I pointed at my feet and spoke for the first time in my life publicly, foolishly, excessively about the ground beneath us. Especially those little estuarine patches of mottled fertility eddying up out of the river banks, I love so. Serpentine ditches of long lush grasses – havens for birds and small animals. Diminutive pockets of Eden at our feet, too small and awkward for man to cultivate or do anything with. The little muddy ducts along which run the rats and ducks and eels; nowhere else are beasts in happier proximity than in these low, Netherlandish slips of paradise. But the antiquarian shrugged at my suggestion as if I had asked him to tell me the history of his own face.

All the same, bravely, he tried to answer me. He rubbed his nose and began, 'A long time ago, as we all know, the sea defences of our Dutch republic were established heroically, permanently.' He stopped, smiled. He began again, 'Ever since those great days, the preservation and care of the dykes have been the prime concern of the republic, and the means by which we have defined ourselves as a people.' He paused. 'There has been no generation that has not laid additional buttresses against this great national monument.' He began again, 'For us, the people of this region, safe in the northern reaches, sitting on more solid ground, beyond the reach of perpetual danger from the sea; our exertions are merely a ritual. We re-line the dykes each year, not in order to resist the futile sea, but simply in order to make demonstration of our conformity.' I liked him better after this attempt to explain our thoughtless habits back to us.

II

International mails came irregularly and always together. Usually packets arrived every three months or so. January was the big month for receiving news from America. Then, all the families who had seen relatives go to the new world would withdraw with their news at more or less the same time, and an air of deep reflection settled over our little town. Nothing more disturbing than domestic scandal ever came our way, and even these were broadcast as soberly as any other piece of news. One family told of their nephew who by someone's curious reckoning had lived with more women than any of his grandparents had grandchildren!

However, the reports from the new world introduced an ambivalence to our consciousness of ourselves. The accumulation of accounts of our kins' experiences in the new world made it harder for us all to tell if we were fortunate or unfortunate, if we were rich or poor, if we were settled according to a way of life that had raised itself over generations to a standard of conscientiousness or whether we were slipping, generation on generation, into the pit of depravity and complacency – unconscious of the extent of our fall. Whether the rector's assessment of our lot was right, or the town drunk's; whether we were happy and blessed or wretched and cursed.

III

Then, one year it was announced that the annual ceremony of relining our dykes was to be superseded for ever. Parliament had commanded that iron sheets replace our medieval wooden planks and boards. A surveyor, sent from the government, arrived in the town to make the measurements for the industrial manufacture of these iron sheets. His appearance generated all sorts of unusual behaviour. The two queens of our little kingdom, M. de Pot and M. de Mot, who had never before acknowledged each other in the street, became inseparable. They linked arms to entertain and divert the surveyor, and would stop him in his work, and tell him, almost speaking in unison, all the little adventures and incidents of our town with which their memories were stuffed. He would invariably say something like, 'It is marvellous how much is going on in a little town like this. Quite marvellous. You don't know how wrong they are in the city who say that nothing happens in a place like this. It is they who are shut in from the world, they who are closed off from one another. They who are mean-spirited and dull, I have always thought this.'

And this lugubrious comedy continued, reaching its apotheosis in one fine, embarrassing moment, when a child's dog got trapped in a mud hole in the estuary. The surveyor was nearby, but didn't pay any attention to the children's calls at first. The cries soon grew desperate, and a crowd quickly gathered around the children. There was lots of agitated shouting; pretty soon the whole town was there offering advice on the best way to save the little dog from drowning. Of course the surveyor was among them by that time, and he expressed himself marvellously satisfied with the reactions of our little town. I think everyone was a little embarrassed by all his ingratiating speeches after this.

IV

Else was my chief friend, though we had not spoken in thirty five years. Of the many good people of our town that it was a pleasure to see and know, Else was the only remarkable one. A spinster, my own age, and the subject still of subdued speculation but only on account of the mysterious, friendless isolation in which she lived.

As children, we had spent all our time with a boy called Todd, a remarkable child whom none of us doubted would grow into a remarkable man. He had been fostered upon the rector, his uncle, when he was five, having lost his parents overseas. Todd brought to me the first conscious thoughts of love I had ever entertained when I found myself wondering why this strange boy from far away seemed to love me. Why he favoured my company so much, when he had so much more in the way of resources and energy than I. Why he chatted away to me about all the wonderful thoughts in his head, when I had so little to reply. He was mine and Else's teacher, and by thinking aloud he showed us what it was to think, to speculate, to wonder. He would discuss stories we had been told in school and enlarge them with his interest. By admiring the things around him, he showed us they existed. He noticed things I would never have noticed for myself; he it was who showed us into those little scurrying patches of rampant, fertile wilderness in the clefts of the rivers and marshes.

Else and I loved Todd. He lived among us like a visitant, examining and admiring every prosaic detail of our circumstance with the rapt attentiveness of an exile. Soon to leave. The last night we were to spend together, we three sat out beneath the wide, starry sky waiting on our final farewell to Todd the next morning. We said little, until Else signalled the moment Todd was to go by declaring, 'We shall find as many reasons to despise each other as there are stars in the sky. The more we succumb to these habits of disparagement, the greater our reliance on the hidden worth of an individual . . .'

With this observation sounding in our ears, Todd embraced us both, and went off.

After Todd's departure, Else and I, aged eighteen, found our closeness embarrassing. We were too intimate to be easy any longer, and our grief over our departed friend inhibited us from starting that courtship which I think, in other circumstances, would have occurred quite naturally between us.

We agreed to see less of each other, and gradually inside two years had stopped meeting or talking at all. She lived entirely by herself, and took part in no affairs in our town. Though no one else could see it, it was plain to me how rich were her thoughts and how well she was supported by her inward life to live in such quietness and solitude. Occasionally, we found ourselves close to each other. At funerals we would always stand nearby one another, not as a profession of intimacy, but I think rather from natural, animal gravity.

I find it hard to give an impression of my admiration of her. She was withdrawn without appearing either modest or shy. Resolute without purpose, as intrinsically beautiful a specimen of the natural world as a tusk of ivory. Her irregular and erratic ways seemed coated by a patina which gave to her least acts a subdued and impalpable richness.

In some way, consciously, I lived to do her honour in my thoughts. I stayed to observe her, believing the world did not contain a more remarkable or a richer person.

V

After some months among us, the surveyor announced his measurements were complete, and he would be leaving us. That we could expect the government teams who would carry out the new works to arrive some time in the next year. We decided to stage a banquet, to say goodbye.

Such festivities do not occur even once in a generation. The weather being fine and reliable, a canopy was erected in our town square, and a table made beneath it at which everyone in the town could expect to find a place. A fine feast was prepared, and served, and enjoyed. There were a few speeches, none very long or interesting, and as the sunlight was fading a small party was invited by the mayor to return to his house. So it was that some fifteen elderly citizens of our little town found themselves closeted in the mayor's rooms, entertaining for the last time the government surveyor. The atmosphere was unusual; an occasion both public and democratic had dissolved into a private party. The awkward sense of our confederacy reduced still further the resources of our conversation.

Needless to say the antiquary dominated the conversation, and it was during one of his tedious speeches that he mentioned the name of Todd W for the first time in the surveyor's hearing. The surveyor, the most distracted among us, leapt on this name as a starving man might leap on a bone. He asked the antiquarian Todd's exact age, exact name, and established that this was the same man he seemed to know. He explained to us all, with great delight, that he did not know him personally, but knew of him by reputation. That Todd W should have hailed from this particular town was a fact entirely unknown to him, and it was a great disappointment to him that he should have made this discovery on the very eve of his departure.

We were all, of course, eager to learn what the surveyor knew of Todd, whom everyone remembered with great fondness, but the surveyor could not satisfy our curiosity. Todd had gone overseas, had lived among savages, and discovered some things – he was not sure what – had disappeared and been presumed lost for several years, and then had re-emerged with more discoveries beneath his belt. The President of the Academy of Natural Sciences had made a toast to him at some banquet, which had passed into the folklore of the capital, and which the surveyor – along with everyone else, he presumed – who had read the banquet written up in the journal of the society's proceedings, would never forget. The president's exact words were, he quoted, 'A lifetime's study has barely afforded me as much pleasure or reward as I took today, on a stroll around the park in the company of Todd W.' Without our knowing it Todd had become our national emblem of intrepidity and ingenuity.

Todd's fame gave the antiquary and the surveyor reason to forget about the rest of us entirely; one or two pairs of eyes I noticed flitting over my face, to gauge my feelings. If I didn't want to challenge the antiquary's right to speak as an authority on Todd's childhood, I certainly didn't want to try and impress the surveyor with my credentials as his friend.

The mayor eventually had enough of it, and told us it was time for us all to leave.

I left the mayor's house and turned to walk along the river, meaning to spend the night out of doors, something I do two or three times each year. The sky was clear, the air was fresh, I looked at the tops of the trees a long time, and then up to the great empty heaven which is always above us. I remembered Else on such a night, when she was young, expressing her astonishing opinion that the universe was the secret hoard of virtue.

I dozed for a little while, sitting with my back against the bottom of a tree and when I woke I found I was thinking of my mother. And in particular of one morning, when my mother came to my bed full of sunshine, and awoke me with a wonderful hug. I thought of my mother and Todd and Else, the compass points of my vicarious courage.

VI

As the dawn started to rise, I began my return along the river path. When I was still far outside the town I saw Else approaching. We were still some distance apart when she recognized me. At first I wondered if she had heard already about the return of Todd's reputation at the mayor's party, and whether she might be looking for me. But it was not possible. No one would dream of bringing her the story so early, nor would anyone know in which direction I was to be found. No, Else would hear this news later in the day. It could only be coincidence that we should meet like this, in seclusion, in the half light of a new dawn, myself in possession of certain facts that somehow would substantiate both our lives.

She would realize later that at this encounter I had known, and that I might have told her. But to step around her was as much as I could do or say. As we edged past each other on the path our eyes met, whatever it was she saw in mine she pressed back with a quiet force still full of wild confidence.

David Hart
Two Poems

THE FORCES ALONG THE BORDER

The forces along the border are on heightened alert,
the flowers you asked to be delivered here are here still,
the A4 sheet that shows the miscopy
of the picture of the rock pools I'd been intending to copy well
is beside my computer still as if it will tell me a poem,
a new surfing deal has arrived on a free CD-ROM,
a few days ago in a charity shop I bought a CD-ROM
called *The Art of Singing*.

There was a phrase arising in me just then,
something like, 'And this reminds me,'
but I'll let that one go. Here is a tiny picture of a tree
I cut from the magazine yesterday, a solitary tree,
a tree in winter in a flat landscape, seen through a window.

At this stage of this poem – the thought has arisen spontaneously,
I'm not working to a formula – I want a shift,
even a bursting out, using perhaps the word *glorious*,
perhaps provoking in the reader a sigh or a gulp even,
a delight, an electric moment: *We've turned a corner*,
and I'd love that to have happened here.

Perhaps I shall end by reversing the lines with which I began:
the miscopy of the picture, the flowers you asked to be delivered,
along the border on heightened alert, the forces.

WE CAME THEN

We came then to the extreme garden,
I took off my hat and you did,
or you took off yours and I did,
you took off your shoes, I took off mine,
without looking at each other at all,
looking at each other the whole time,

then you said, *Write this, this now,*
or I said it, we spread our coats on the grass,
sat facing the inner garden
and looked at each other
      for the first time again.
       Rain came,
we sat and got wet, the flowers shone,
water dripped down our eyes, I said,
      Do write this, this now,
or you said it. The paths made holy patterns,
you sneezed or I did,
there was a toothbrush in the dog daisies,
I pointed to the ferns, or you did,
we walked the extent of it
      until we became giddy
with eyes, I would have brought you a chair,
you would have brought one for me,
we said together, *It will rain for ever,*
you touched my hand
with your finger, or I touched yours
with mine, we kept walking,
there was no horizon,
I said, *What next?*, quietly, or you did.

Bernardine Evaristo
The Burial Ground

An excerpt from Soul Tourists, *a forthcoming novel*

Stanley had buried his father, in a field of dumb bedfellows whose sole purpose was to provide balanced nutrition for the more vulnerable members of the animal kingdom – the invertebrates, who ate with the slow, sarcastic knowledge that dinner really wasn't going anywhere. They were the subterranean militia of revenge, whose communal memory stored the cruel holocaust of their various insect species by predictable versions of swat: shoe, garden implement, rolled up newspaper, cricket bat.

Mr Clasford Williams Esq. was the newest fully paid-up resident of Tower Hamlet's community of gourmet cadavers, whose social relationships to each other were defined only by proximity and the fact that their hearts, in one breathtaking moment, had stopped.

Here Clasford would crave his daily cocktail of whisky and beer, as rainwater – sullied by stones and dirt, soaking through his rotting oak coffin with its oyster-coloured lining, through the linen safari suit he'd brought with him in 1965, when *mi fus come a dis blasted country* – would finally seep down to accentuate his thirst and accelerate the decay of brown skin that had been, for seventy-seven years, his formal application to British society, determining his acceptance or rejection, something he was always going on about. The transformation from fully qualified chemist in his home country to postman in his adopted one – never quite overcome. That and the trajectory of Stanley from grammar school boy, to university graduate, to landing a plum job in the city with good prospects and a weekly pay cheque that Clasford himself could never earn in a whole month of rising at 4 a.m. to sort out the post at the depot. If it was a slap on the back Stanley craved.

'Ongle a man like mi can produce pickney like oonoo. So doan swell y' head and tink say y' boots bigger dan mine.'

'Hardly likely,' Stanley muttered.

To which Clasford would reply, drawing his arm back as if to hit him,

'Awa yu say?'

'Nuttin,' Stanley mumbled, shuffling out of the room, hearing his father have the last word, as always, as he walked down the corridor.

'Leave de bwai alone, Clasford,' his mother Pearline would interject. 'Mi know say yuh proud like lion for im. We *both* are, Stanley,' she shouted after him.

'I shoulda let him roam street. Woulda end up in de chink by now,' added his father, topping his mother in volume.

Now, when Clasford turned over in his sleep towards the heavenly body of Pearline, who had preceded him underground by five years; when he reached out to caress her ample, blue nylon softness, she would not respond warmly to him with a cajoling. 'Yuh tink yuh can manage it, Ole Bwai?' Or resist with sleepy irritation, 'Mi not in de *mood*, Clasford!' Pearline, who was lying peacefully beneath him, had turned into nothing more than a bag of celibate bones. Nor would he sweat at night, as he had done all his married life, drenching the sheets, and Pearline, who would complain that he'd give her rheumatism 'one-a dese days.'

Storm clouds had been rallying forces all morning on this windswept east London plateau. Its sprawling perimeter overhung by trees with brown, red and golden leaves floating to the ground. In the distance were tower blocks, which rendered an otherwise pastoral scene inescapably urban. The city fathers converged, broke off into splinter groups, flaunted their double-breasted chests, puffed up with the arrogance of knowing that a few dobs of well aimed spittle was enough to warn the mourners below of their omnipotence.

Stanley wished the sky would split open into a terrible storm, for hailstones and lightning, for weather so dramatic that the feelings raging inside him were matched, indeed dwarfed, indeed erased by the roaring elements. He wore a new black suit purchased the day before, and his long legs were astride the heap of earth beside the hole into which the coffin had been lowered and inside which was the man he had last seen in the mortuary's viewing room, which had made him feel, for the first time in his life, infernally mortal.

He had entered the small, pine-panelled room, with the atmospheric mood lighting of a chapel. Its background music was the hum of an air conditioner, with a flashing red light, especially designed for dead bodies on display. In the far corner, a vase contained a spray of violet lilacs and white lilies on an elegant metal plinth.

As he crossed the threshold his body shrank like a cartoon figure, losing two thirds of his height and bulk, disappearing into too-big clothes and shuffling in grown-up shoes. Unthinkingly, the un-broken voice of his childhood squeaked, 'Hello Daddy,' accompanied by a wild deluge of tears.

Stanley was immediately immersed in the most intimate communion with the man before whom he would never, ever cry.

Clasford Williams was tucked up into a purple drape with gold crosses embroidered at its side. His head rested on a white pillow. His face, a dark matt brown, was so old yet so unlined, skin moulded smoothly over cheekbones that poor diet made overly prominent, and his jaw line was as stubborn in death as it had been in life, tensile. His wild grey bush of hair had been cut close to his head, his wild grey beard had been trimmed into a neat goatee. His lips, which in his last years drooped listlessly away from his few remaining bottom teeth, had been tightly tucked in by the undertaker, making them thinner. His face still exuded a restrained fierceness, for after only a few hours of death, his body still contained something of the spirit that had been within him. Surely this is what Stanley could sense, or did the life force that made eyes shine with light from the miracle of creation, that gave skin its sheen, really just disappear so quickly, without even a lingering trace, after over seventy years? Just like that.

Clasford hadn't turned his head as he entered. Jackson

expected him to. He expected his usual brusque manner, for his voice to say with the familiar tone that carried both threat and approval with measured weight, 'Mi know oonoo bin behavin' yerself.' But he ignored him. Not a lopsided smile. Not a rant. Not a reprimand or provocation. Stanley moved closer. Here was death at close range. He touched his father's brow fleetingly, it was deep-frozen. Two slits of eyes showed spookily beneath his closed lids. They hadn't shut them properly!

Stanley's urge was to pick him up in his big arms and cradle him. Would he be stiff and light? He would be cold. Would he melt as he held him, turn back to water and pour himself over him.

He looked so frail. So dignified. So.

He sat down on the seat at the side, a box of tissues had been provided on a little table, and he was overwhelmed with a compassion that he never knew was in him. 'I'm so sorry,' he cried aloud, 'I'm so sorry, Daddy.'

He sat there and let it all flow out of him, wanting to stay close to his father's presence that had always been there, like air, like memory, like skin, like earth, like birth. Realizing that now he would feel him even more acutely.

Realizing he was only human after all.

Paul Magrath
Reviewing

I'm reading a book
For pleasure and profit

The pleasure is variable
The profit small

I'm doing what's called
Reviewing.

image: the hetton-le-hole bookclub - betty long
<betty@thepoetrycubicle.org.uk>

Jason Cowley
Against the Grain

Reflections of a Literary Editor

Anyone working or writing for the *New Statesman* today operates in what can be described only as the long aftermath. There is a powerful feeling that the best is in the past: that a small weekly magazine devoted to politics and culture must inevitably struggle to find its place in our overlit, celebrity-driven media landscape. When the *New Statesman* reached the peak of its circulation in the mid-to-late 1960s, scarcity had a value: there were very few places in which a group of people with a common interest in culture and politics could meet to discuss ideas or swap notes on the latest book, play or film. If you had something to say or merely wished to be kept informed about the society in which you lived, you invariably turned to the *New Statesman* – and perhaps, to a lesser extent, *The Spectator* and *Encounter*. The *New Statesman* was the place in which the academy, Parliament, journalism and the common reader would meet. There was nowhere else to go.

My father, from a traditional east London working-class family (his own father was a bus driver), conveyed well the excitement he used to feel on buying the *New Statesman* as a young man; here, he felt, was his potential route of entry to a gilded world. He believed – like so many of his immediate post-war generation – in progress, that you could remake yourself through hard work and a commitment to education. He was Leonard Bast or Gordon Comstock: someone for whom reading and writing was a heroic activity, even if his family background meant that he had little or no chance of a university education.

This was of course a time before the emergence of multi-section newspapers, with their own dedicated books and arts supplements; before the arrival of style magazines such as *The Face* and *Esquire*; before the creation of the *London Review of Books*; a time when the *Times Literary Supplement* still published unsigned reviews, and before the fragmentation of television and radio. In those days, it was possible to talk of a common culture. It was still possible to assume that your family and friends were reading the same newspapers and magazines as you, discussing the same plays and television programmes and listening to the same radio shows. Such things are no longer possible; ours is a generation addicted to abundance, to the tyranny of choice. We are repeatedly told that we want more of everything – and that is what we get: more sections in our newspapers, more television channels to watch, more books to buy, more magazines to read.

Today there is an absence at the centre of our culture, where first religion and then progressive ideas used to be. The great schemes to remake the world – Marxism, socialism, liberalism, environmentalism – have largely failed. We no longer really believe in progress, or in the perfectibility of the human animal. What we have, instead, is a kind of perpetual disenchantment, as exemplified by the aimless rebellion of the antiglobalization movement. Also, that which once occupied the margins of the culture – football, celebrity, television, the media itself – is now at its very centre. If there is a common culture today, it revolves around football and artificial media events such as *Pop Idol* or *Big Brother*. What place the *New Statesman* – and indeed the book review – in such a post-political age?

Before joining the *New Statesman*, where I work part-time as the literary editor (two to three days each week) – I was a staff writer on *The Times*, and before that a journalist on *The Bookseller*, the weekly news magazine for the book business. For most of my journalistic life, I have therefore written about writers and the writing life, though not exclusively, as I also very much enjoy reporting and travelling. I'm often asked the purpose of book reviews and whether they make a difference. Well, Evelyn Waugh once had this advice for a young writer, 'Reviews matter very little in the case of a novel. The important thing is to make people talk about it. You can do this by forcing your way into newspapers in some other way.' His words are perhaps more true today than they have ever been – because the surest way to enter public consciousness (and the bestseller list) is for a writer to liberate him or herself from the ghetto of the books pages and, in some way, to become news. Which means those writers with a dramatic personal story, very good looks, or who are already famous, are immediately privileged.

There were more than 116,000 books published in Britain last year, most of which enjoyed only a brief public presence, and were certainly not reviewed at all, before beginning that short, brutal journey to the remainder bin – from where only the oblivion of the pulping pit awaits. If you have ever visited a pulping warehouse, as I did recently, you will understand the melancholy that accompanies the witnessing of such mechanized destruction. The destruction of books. Watching this happen one thinks often of the American poet Delmore Schwartz who, disillusioned by his own literary failure, wrote: 'No reputation is more than snowfall; it vanishes.'

Yet much of the appeal of publishing is its speculative nature; it thrives on risk, the unexpected and on the bi-annual renewal of hope. No publisher can ever know which of their books, even those supported by a marketing budget, will succeed. Which perhaps explains why the phenomenon of word-of-mouth recommendation is so important to the book business. And choosing a book for review, even if that review is less than favourable, is one small way of helping a book to find its public place, from where it may or may not be recommended.

The *New Yorker* journalist Malcolm Gladwell, in his witty little book *The Tipping Point* (Little, Brown: 2000) – itself something of a word-of-mouth success – suggests the best way to understand the emergence of fashion trends, the ebb and flow of crime waves or the transformation of unknown books into bestsellers, is to think of them as epidemics: 'Ideas and products and messages and behaviours spread just like viruses.' In this sense, we contaminate one another with preferences and recommendations. The 'tipping point' is reached as a social epidemic becomes contagious and crosses a threshold to reach critical mass. From there nothing can stop it catching on and spreading. 'The world of the tipping point' he writes, 'is a place where the unexpected becomes expected, where radical change is more than a possibility. It is – contrary to all our expectations – a certainty!'

It's a neat idea, but would that it were that simple. If publishers knew how to start and control what Gladwell calls 'positive epidemics', then publishing wouldn't be the frustrating, often profligate business that it is. Fewer than ten per cent of all titles from a particular list make a profit, which means that most books are published at a loss. Even fewer books are reviewed.

How does one choose which books to review and which to ignore? Some of my colleagues on *The Times* were surprised when I joined the *New Statesman* at the end of 1998: they could not understand why I would walk away from a staff job on a powerful institution such as *The Times* for a part-time opportunity on what was then perceived to be an insecure, struggling magazine. But I was steeped in the history of the *New Statesman* and moved by the challenge I'd be set by its editor, Peter Wilby: to help revive and modernize this once great magazine. Part of that challenge was to return the *New Statesman*, not exactly to the centre of the culture – that would be impossible – but to help it once more to enter the national cultural conversation, which, on the whole, we have succeeded in doing: the magazine is now selling more copies than it has done for at least twenty years, our articles and reports are regularly followed up by the national and international media, our pages are full of animated contrarians and we have even been making a small profit.

What I have done on the books pages is to follow not a British, but an American model – by publishing a long weekly lead review (between 1500 and 3500 words) and then a selection of shorter reviews, which offer a change of pace and a diversity of subject matter. The pages, I concede, reflect my own interests: philosophy, history, current affairs, science, fiction and popular culture in the widest sense, which may include anything from sport to fashion. They are not especially literary, in the sense of being high-bourgeois – I have little desire to read a review of, say, a collection of Auden's prose or yet another book about one of the Bloomsbury group. Nor are the pages interested in hard left wing posturing – I respond to wit, mischief, and maverick voices, from left or right. I have brought together a small squad of distinguished regular reviewers – including John Gray, professor of European thought at the London School of Economics; Will Self; the young Oxford philosopher, Edward Skidelsky; Pankaj Mishra; Richard Gott, once of *The Guardian*; Mick Hume, former editor of *Living Marxism* magazine; Robert Winder, a former literary editor of *The Independent*; Jan Morris; Kathryn Hughes, the biographer and critic; Malcolm Rifkind; Hugo Barnacle; Zoe Williams; Suzanne Moore; Anthony Howard; and, before her death, the great Elizabeth Young – whose opinions are invariably bold and unpredictable. I have tried to encourage the small presses and adventurous independents such as Serpent's Tail and the recently launched Atlantic Books. And I have tried, not always successfully, to offer space to younger reviewers, as one seeks to find the next James Wood or – if only – VS Pritchett. (If you know of a candidate, please let me know.)

Unlike being on a newspaper, I'm left entirely alone by my editor, free to publish what I want and by whom I wish. The only pressure I feel is to produce provocative and entertaining pages. So yes, I do believe that book reviews matter: that through choosing the right books the literary editor can use his or her pages to offer readers a sense of new thinking and new ideas emerging from the universities; to introduce good writing on a range of subjects into the magazine, few of which are tied to that week's news; and to create a community of readers who believe in the enduring power of the word and who wish to participate in a cultural conversation, however muted that may be.

Hilary Davies
Imperium

I: Kent. Chatham Docks

Walter Hall of England,
These, rigged, are your deities
As we go aboard this frosty morning
And the dockers load in the kegs.
Flex calves, spine, ankles
Up into the tarry sparrings
To measure out the sky.
Medway, winter midway, silver draining down to cold Sheerness,
Rocking the castle cliffs and battlements
At Rochester as we sway off the tide.
The shrouds are burning: like St Elmo's fire
The frost licks along the ratlines
Whilst, up aloft, the main top men
Unfurl the courses, and, running along the yards,
Set staysail, topgallant, starlings flying in the bare blue sky.

*

Imperium

Look. Up here's like nowhere else
Under heaven. Lean into the ice-still air.
What satrap, fanned upon his couch of feathers
Surveys this, the dominion of the shipwright
Whose forests stalk to the sea?
Open the seasoning sheds: Memel, Riga, Stettin,
Leaf mould of the Baltic rising in the air
Like alcohol. Swart. Musk.
The grains are fishscales where the adze cuts through,
A brindled rib of armour to the waves.
Rip-rasp, rip-rasp: rites out of the sawing pits –
With your hand along the bole to feel
Where timber compasses a curve
For futtock, frame, knees to brace
A dancing hull in the sea.

The Prentice Sawyer's Lament

Under it all I saw in this hole:
Bit piece for payment, log by log,
A ten hour log each day from my life stole
O Lord, have mercy on us.

Stand here: learn how the blood runs into pain,
Arms up and back, up, back, until the muscles
Are their own cat-o'-nine-tails trained
O Lord, have mercy on us.

No sky nor air. The sawdust falls like rain.
Wet cloak in winter. In the summer sun
A cloud of choking midges in the brain
O Lord, have mercy on us.

Now in the mornings, a foul flux like silt
Spits from my lungs. The oak is hard to breathe.
Upon my back the wooden walls are built.
O Lord, have mercy on us.

*

Turn three-quarters through this compass;
The steam of men begins to shimmer over dry dock,
Victualling yards. Careful to truss
These flailing oxen tight out over the terrifying water:
Smell how they dung with fear. Truckles rattle
As the hemp curls in, like those port-maidens
Sailors coming off the tropics
Clasp in their restless hammocks,
Upon whose flaxen rope-bands they'll climb up the stars.
We shift a little on the mooring lines:
It's spring-tide ready. The slightest breeze.
Our captain writes dispatches to his querulous wife.
'When wind gets north of westwards, there's our chance
To glide anew upon our medium
And find the sea as wolves track their prey.'
Amidships, bustle where John Wilson, master,
Assesses sandglass, leadlines, charts,
His own wisdom for navigating Gillingham,
Pynam; eyes closed, in his mind along the mudflats
Whether to drift or dredge, what sail
And how to keep away from leeward
At the sighting of Hoo church spire
– Under the yew tree lies my father,
Eager for the surging sound of canvas,
Backstays creaking, the smell of tar –
'Mr Wilson, up anchor, man the bars.
We'll take her now; the weather's favourable
And I and all the men high in blood
For action. Raise the red ensign.
We join Hood.'

Imperium

II: NORFOLK. BURNHAM THORPE

A web of water. Here, vetch, saxifrage
And the tourtourelle cordon the land
Against it. Safe lines of linden trees,
Flint steeple, the backed-up rectangles
Of stall, barn, forge, which demarcate
Certainty, the known interior,
Children raising their butterfly nets forever
On the grass.

                  At night only, first a shurring
At the edge of windowpane, fainter than conches.
It's not the feet of the mists over Dogger,
Or this silk rain like a lover's hand,
But the sound of something undertowing
That draws us through the lens of everyday
Onto the huge horizons. Open this window
And hang into the stinging air. Far out,
A kind of boom beyond the rise
Is more than storm, a sempiternal tug and flow,
World heartbeat whose chords wrap round the oceans.
Fair, on a big white day of wind,
The spit of sand bordering blue
And waves as tall as houses. How high the heart too,
Bowling cartwheels down the dunes
And racing veins of silver mud along the channels.
Curlew. Curlew. Where do they come from?
Cockleboats from Brancaster, wherries from Stiffkey,
Tern cambered between Arctic, Antarctic,
Strandwalking here.
Get in and keep the oars free
Of eelgrass, move now plashing down runnels
Whose tides drive St Lawrence, Hudson, Rio San Juan.

III: Whitehall. Admiralty

'Sirs,

       My great exertions, in the name of country,
When stationed on the Leeward Isles,
Should show my mettle. Finding outrageous
The colouring of American ships for British
To trade illegally fish, timber, grain against those products
Rightfully won from our plantations,
I seized the schooner, *Brilliant*, and brigs
Impertinently leeching off our state.
I had no thought, when I defended England's honour,
To be so poorly served as writs, confinement,
And threats against my money and my person.
Yet duty, law, uphold my actions surely.
Of this I'm certain: I have ever been a zealous officer
And this must bring reward. Perplexing that my letters
Offering service meet with no answer and yet
The corridors of Admiralty cluster and chatter
With business as I sit idle in this ante-room.
There's war bustle: commissions, ships refitted,
Messengers running up and down to signal
Along the telegraph this excitement bouncing
From hill to hill, all the way to gleaming Portsdown
And the unbearable, longed-for sea.
Give me a cockleboat, sirs, and I'll be grateful.
I stand ready, ready: let me away from domesticity
And the futile garden; everything indicates war.'

Imperium

IV: Glamorgan. Merthyr Tydfil

Rattle over the moors, past the crofts grinding rye,
A summer evening allowing us not to notice
Too much those shacks and scraggy animals
But rather admire how fierce the waters
Burn down the rockface, drilling that splendid force
Necessary for the casting of guns.
How the mountains beetle, and the crags sublime!
Over the lip of Cefn-Coed we see it.
A double sun glaring on the twilit sky,
Unnaturally placed, unmoving, angry.
That's where the river runs – off the beacons
Down to its coal-bearing bed and its furnaces.
Descend. Walls range to meet us like the palisades
Of undeciphered empires, sweating clinker souls.
These hollows where white children's faces stare
Are houses' eyes put out; and sweet Taff trails a grease
Of effluent, spittle, faeces, along its gutters
To the next in line. We are at war:
The furnace burns to pound the mechanisms
Of prosperity and its defences, to found
The iron in the mould so we may draw
The trade nets to us and be rich.

*

David Davies, foundry worker

'I make patterns-patent. It's skilled work.
My dad just stoked. His English wasn't good
Coming from up the Neuadd. That hamlet's gone
Since he left. Walked barefoot off the sheep moors
When they died, along the old drovers' trail
To Merthyr. Hot work, he said, but at least it kept you warm
And there was more space then, more like a family And pigs
behind the cottages, a bit of grass.
No worse than being a blacksmith: lots moved down then

'Cos they had the knack of metal.
The French changed that; at least, it seemed it was.
All up and down where fields were said the owners
More and more coal must come and feed the forges
Grown huge as cathedrals, the men like insects
Day and night beneath the chimneys.
And then the streets –
It is another sort of village now, bloated
From all proportion, turned to grey
'Cept for the nightly burning mountain,
And where the salmon used to rise,
Back to back houses, bedrooms sweet with sickness,
The women gone rotten from dragging coal trolleys
And the too much drink.
Lord Nelson came: that was a fine treat
For the Guests and Crawshays did fireworks up in their parklands
And those that weren't working could go in and watch.
We got cake, too, and extra measures of beer for each family
But the best of it was his visit into the foundry
To see for himself how we do.
The boys were so proud
By the bellows; even he, who has witnessed
Ships turned to torches, shrank back
As the doors inched wide to let him gaze
At the white-hot rivers that harden to guns.
And then a roar went up. "I do warm work
For England" – so, he gestured, with his hand –
"But you're the Titans of the battleground,
My heartsmiths, dragons of the wooden walls."
His horses slewed, ungainly, up the cobbles,
Rain slated black, and smokestacks shut him out.'

Imperium

V: ON THE MEDITERRANEAN

'No frigates. Since Toulon, a blue desert of anxiety
On what is yet familiar as the little creeks
And pools of Overy Staithe, and, it seems,
As easy for a great invasion's armament
To move by waterboatman stealth
Upon the surface.
                              No frigates.
                                        Without a squadron's eyes
I run blinder than the mangled Spanish bulls
That turned me sick at Cadiz once. Artillery,
Draught-horses, artificers, forty thousand troops in transports,
But also mathematicians, linguists, ancient historians
And astronomers. This force is set for empire,
But which course? Pierces my mind at night like a beacon.
Is it Constantinople for the Bosphorus
And coralling up of Russia? That's defensive,
Not what this man wants or does.
Where else along the Mediterranean opens a crack
To overlordship? At Malta the knights tittle-tattle
Behind the giant defences of their predecessors,
Algiers can only watch the Straits from far off,
A kind of second, lazy, sultry player:
Distracting, yes, but the spoils are poor.
As for the Two Sicilies: ports, provisions,
A striking place across the Mediterranean;
Like a pontoon bridge of islands
That chain's to be broken and kept clear.
But none of this warrants these locust armies
Descending, not even Egypt in her degraded state.
No, some enterprise that covets wealth,
Fecundity, the accumulated science of nations,
Moves here across the Middle Sea in search of prey.
I cannot countenance but it must be beyond
These spheres of influence, through Giza, Cairo,
And the mosquito swamps of Suez to our Indian colonies
There to steal the very heart of empire from us.'

VI: Egypt. Aboukir Bay

'Fair breezes; weather clear. At one
Saw Alexandria's decayed towers
And lighthouse that once lit the world
The merest stump above the souks and mudhuts.
Beneath it float the spars and rigging of the enemy.
Intolerable to think Napoleon's escaped to the Red Sea,
Me to have let him go through my own impetuousness,
Irritable reluctance to play cunning, lie in wait.
Signals. Ball in the Alexander: "Got close in to harbour.
Two ships of the line, six frigates with French colours hoisted;
Main fleet disappeared."
Only Aboukir on this brackish,
Sand-spitted shore can hold them surely.
Afternoon drawing on, and running brisk along the coast.
The Zealous flags, "Sixteen first rate sail at anchor,
Bearing East by South." Drop leads and sounding.
Haul the wind to larboard, unbend the best bower cable
Through the sternpost. Now we must fight.'

*

Imperium

Almost soft, the light, and so close into shore
You'd swear the bray of donkeys, camels,
Mingled in the swish of water, and the sails breathed balsam;
A bay so shallow as we round the headland
That fish flash silver between the menace of our hulls gliding
And the cloudy rocks.
The yards creak and clack
As we move closer, closer. What overtopping towers,
What rake of pinnacles, shifting like great oaks in winter
Stare at us! L'Orient, more a metropolis set free
Upon a mirror than the foul-smelling coop of fear
I know she is, shows all her aviary of ensigns flying.
I hear men coughing tightly, orders –
Small, staccato, given as from far off,
Out of another time when all was theory
And no man imagined the configuration
Would be just *this* beach, *this* curve of battleships,
This incendiary going down of the sun.

The wind is in our favour: we all know
There'll be no waiting for an uncertain dawn.
This must turn us into dread nightriders
Who see and strike and capture in the dark.
Most difficult of all: how to dislodge them
From their starched lines and pickets –
Gunports yapping open and the scent of flame –
We tack towards them gingerly, each captain's eye
Upon the unforgiving, unknown shallows
That ruin, and wink a creamy, siren blue.
The French fleet swing a little; their cable buoys
Bob long towards the shoals, and clank, and clank and pull . . .
Just long enough. Foley upon his charts exultant
For six fathoms through the Bequier roads
Flashes from studding sail to fort to shoal to vanship
And, as a peregrine drops, sheers down the rush of air
To kill. Round *Guerrier* he drives,
Glimpses the spruce, swing features of her figurehead
Before his gunners blow her face to splinters,

Winnowing them like javelins down all the bulkheads,
Slicing, disembowelling, opening men's groins
Westwards, the sun setting turns her sails to walls of flame.

*

How many hours since we first came into the gloom,
Hearing above us the roar like cascades of thunder
And muffled boom of vulcan pistons?
Behind the gates of horn, deformed phantoms
Bend and pack sulphur bags for the crater of war.
And the blackened bird boys take it there.
'Water! Gunner's wife, give me some!
                              Draw off my fatigue!'
She leans it to me, breasts bare, too tired for shame.
Of a sudden, carpenter's screaming, 'John! *John!*
Over here! Up the walk! A breach! Christ! *Christ!*
Quickly, for God's sake!' Shoulders grunting
As we force the timber in and scramble hammers
To the sheets of lead. 'Where's Bobby?' 'Haven't seen him.'
'You don't suppose . . .?' The sea and sulphur suck
                              the air we breathe.
'He's here.' 'Where?' Under a knee of the orlop,
In a dark, juddering overhang, jiggling, gesticulating,
Sitting in his friend's brains.
                              'Get out' a there, man!'
'This way – leave him alone! There's some that needs
A bugger's help down here more'n he'll warrant.'
The sweating cockpit: midshipman John Taylor,
Only fifteen, whimpering for Mama, his face blown away;
Captain Faddy, wide-eyed and gurgling,
Just one purplish nick across his throat.
And strong Joe Gilmour, with his hip laid bare,
Who lasted two hours without tourniquet,
Bellowing for aid.
                              This the mover at the heart of it:
Our surgeon, Blackleys, one-time apothecary, friend,
– A man we trust 'cos he's that mindful

Imperium

To our little ailments and takes great pains
To give us air, fight, decent broth with fevers –
How he's become Hephaestus, massive
In the furnace of unmaking, as with his knife
And saw he butchers, and the world shrieks red.

*

Night over Egypt and the Mediterranean.
Carronades punch the air. *Bellerophon*'s drifting.
Maststumps scaffold the sky. In Bruey's cabin,
The compasses and charts chequer with heat
And set the logbook curling in the choking air.
At first, leisurely, delicate, a devouring
Of luxury that goes unnoticed: decanters crack,
Burn blue, and from the leather rises a stink of tanneries,
Urine, suffering.
                    'Look here! Beneath the door!
Black smoke! What's happening in there?'
Marines come running with a broken spar
To batter through. 'Get ready. One. Two. Heave!'
A flash and crack of firetongue reaches out
And lights them all to spinning wicks of pain,
Leaps to the gangways, out onto the poop
And up the rigging, O Corpus Sanctum,
O St Elmo's fire, this night no laudes,
No good augury, The sails are cliffs of flame,
Her masts' trinity glowing like a tinder-tree,
Beams blowing with report of cannon
All the way down to Alexandria.
Souls, save yourselves. Strip naked; edge down
The anchor chains to where the waters burn
Hotter than the flickering crucible of desert.
L'Orient's skeleton, like a leaf scorching in the fire,
Is become her own Eastern light and chapel ardent,
Blazing catafalque floating on the passionless sea.

VII: KINGDOM OF THE TWO SICILIES. NAPLES

Black, treacherous footing along the arsenal quay:
Poseidon and his nereids leer from cornerstones
In the torchlight, and whip their livid crests
Across the bay. The city breathes shadows.
Admirals and kings in this unfamiliar place
Grow cold, and startle when the wind drifts
Brouhaha from the Piazza del Mercato.
What was that footstep in the gutter,
Rasp along the stone? Boots clink in the vaults
And up the stairs – just three months gone
Since champagne laughter pirouetted in these florid halls
For Marquis Nile and Viscount Pyramid –
Whisperings. Under the silks, the stink of fear.
'Keep silent.' Armies boom in their heads.
'I *will* have reprisals when we do return.
Severity like your monarch's to the Irish
To be demonstrated; especially the females
Treated without pity.' A white-haired sister's
Head remembered, bellowed by the republican crowd.

'Hurry, the storm's rising. No time to lose.'
Coffers, damasks, Greek antiquities, squashed
Under tarpaulins; in the canvas cots retch courtiers
And infants begin to ebb from women's arms.
Round Capri under an indigo sky
And into winter on the fierce Tyrrhenian:

Slam of wind and water, Lungs flatten, fight to breathe.
Like bobbins, the six-storied warships flip end-on;
Men break against the rails. On all sides open
The grim honeycombs of whirlpool
Down which the hallucinating eye swoops to death.

Christ of the Deep, your arms outstretched
Against the currents, and your mother,
Star of and married to the sea, stand between us

Imperium

And the smoking maelstrom, be our bulkhead
And keen keel cutting through the riptides,
For without you the disingenuous and shabby heart
Spins like an *ignis fatuus* in the night.

VIII: Kingdom of the Two Sicilies. Palermo, Palazzino Cinese

'An absurdity of peacock feathers, monkeys dressed as ministers
And philosophers as donkeys, peep-bo cockatoos
And jumped-up whores, The Queen a compact
Of venality, licentiousness, and a gargantuan
Desire for power; her consort, Ferdinand,
Distinguished only by the hecatombs of animals
He decorates his vulgar court with.

                                   God help us
If these must be our allies. And why an Englishman
Should linger in these unwholesome places
And rot himself with drink and cardtables
Is beyond belief. He will not out
To attend his duty, says he "shall not expose"
Their Serene Majesties nor their kingdom to conquest
By the godless revolutionaries.

                                What is he thinking of?
With French escaped from Brest to join the Spanish
– An enemy fleet of forty-two ships of the line –
He dares to cock a snook at his superiors
And write 'he has no scruples in deciding
Better to save the kingdom of Naples and risk Minorca"
Than leave these petty tyrants in order to protect England's lynchpin
In this blockade! Is he become so befuddled,
Effeminized by honours, flattery, all these ridiculous baubles
That whirr and click and twinkle like a fairground carousel?
His counsel's shot to pieces: as if a man who'll brave for years
The privations of a battleship and agonies of war
Should cuddle meekly as a lapdog to the bosom
Of the first ambitious cozener who comes along.

It's risible. This gap-toothed hero with his ambassador's moll
Who shrills and ecstasies in Merseyside Italian,
Every day fatter and more incongruous than a bullock
Draped in organdie. And vicious with it:
A kind of blinded spite towards any not partisan enough
To participate in this vainglorious fug.
Take last night: how seamen who've been fighting
Thirty years blenched to see her kiss the Turkish sword
Foul with Jacobin blood; one captain gagged,
And others muttered, "Shame!"
But she's exultant; flounces off her attitudes
Unblushingly, and puffs the scent of self-conceit
Up into his acquiescing, wizened face.'

IX: AT SEA. OFF MONTE CHRISTI

Separated from all I hold precious in the world
What is the use of living, dear friend of my bosom,
Without your darling embrace? Thinking on that night
You led me through the freezing halls
And whispered of such abandonments
As I had never felt nor dreamed of:
This sets my head, my spine, my loins, on fire.
How gently you unclothed and kissed me –
The embers warm and aromatic in the grate –
And loved beyond my deformity and blindness
Into the heart's fortress. Emma, Emma,
My wife before God, my guide, with whom my mind and person
Stand in perfect union, you who alone of women
Could have taken those sweetest liberties with me
No other ever dared, I kiss you fervently
And trust, when we meet again – please God! –
Tomorrow, to find you faithful
For no love is like mine towards you.

Imperium

X: KINGDOM OF THE TWO SICILIES.
NAPLES HARBOUR

'The Prince Caracciolo asks for clemency?
What outrage to propriety is this?
Look at these charges, the man's history:
A noble title, dedicated service both to Naples
And the English king – remember how his ship, *Tancredi*,
Fought alongside us off Leghorn just four years ago?
I learnt to know him then: a commodore
Of bravery and talent, proud Neapolitan,
Impetuous but true in endeavour.
How much he showed this when he helped save
The Sicilian kingdom and we planned together
Their Majesties' escape! Such a man
Of monarch and the people as any fleet commander
Would count himself happy to inherit,
An officer you could call brother and embrace.

Now he begs for clemency.
                                    Brought on board
In peasant disguise and taken on the run,
A renegade, Jacobin sympathizer, a traitor
To his former self, who fired on his own frigates,
And urged the upstart intelligentsia
To think themselves equal to government,
Democrats. Such mutiny makes him a monster:
As if an English admiral had gone amongst the men
At Spithead and preached Tom Paine from the quarterdeck,
Hurra'd them on to raise the Tree of Liberty!
No: he hangs as a common felon from the foreyard arm,
This is my direction: no indulgence, no firing squad
To confer legitimacy or status, no stay to allow
Him to compose his mind, and, when it's done,
His body cut down, weighted, and thrown into the sea.'

Dragged from the polaccas – no privies, seven days
Unshielded from the sun – and over cobbles
To the marketplace: the fine fleur of Naples.
Today not pig's blood in the runnels,
Nor the red eyes of bullocks popping in fear,
But seamstresses, carpenters, garlic sellers,
Nails encrusted where they claw necks and faces,
And knuckles blue from hitting bone.
'There's that bitch, Fonseca: rip her tits bare
So we can have a gander; show 'er what all that learning's
Really good for, eh?' 'Pass her along.'
Botch between the thighs. 'Come on!
What harm's a bit of pleasure when you're going to swing?
Just minutes now; here, make the most of it!'
Thrust. The onlookers roar. Upon the scaffolding
Two dwarves masturbate.
                                        'That's it then. String her up.'
They shimmy down the poles
To steady neck to rope, kick bench away
And caper on her shoulders as she strangulates.

Out in the bay, Caracciolo bears upright through the waters,
His sockets staring at a transfixed king.

XII: LONDON. HOLBORN

'Twins. The prodigality of providence turned curse.
Too weighty for our balance this unexpected
Double grasp on life, the yell and force
Of two necessities. Too much to ask
Of my position, a too scandalous parade
Of what has gone on here. Choice:
He wants a child to bind him to me,
To give him in his middle age a spyglass to the future,
A chance, a dream of domesticity,
Away from cannons and the jealous sea.
But this second child's ruin. I can't afford it.
So, I choose: this first-born to sweetmeats,
Dandling upon her daddy's knee;
The other I dedicate to London city,
The mercy of the metropolis' to and fro.'

London city. A close carriage. Nine o'clock at night.
The squeak and roll upon the cobbles
As we pull away. Down Piccadilly
With its nightwatchmen saluting, Haymarket's
Pleasure girls, toothless and perfumed with gin –
'Mister, hey, mister, will you walk in St James' Park, sir?'
Men unbuttoning themselves as she braces her legs
Against a tree – to Whitehall. What bobs and tracery
Beneath the painted vaults, chandeliers in wine
And First Lord of the Admiralty entertaining
Bumpers to the genius of Copenhagen and the King.
Swing east. Along the Strand, that foreshore
Of not quite between two cities, emporium
Of glitter, windowpanes, the shop assistant helping
To purchase lace from Bruges, tea from Nanking.
And that beyond, the docks and wash of moiré grease
Against green moorings, the scum, heavy loading,
Rank of tallow, tar. Pfauw! The night can't hide
What happens here: how butchers empty lights
And entrails into this trickle, thick with blood

And plastered down with buttocks on their seats of ease.
The rubbish from the market too thrown over,
Cabbage tops, starved dogs, mildewed potatoes,
Fleet ditch where the foundling hospital stands.
We've come. Lamps flicker behind the cordoned gate.

'Take her and make sure she's baptized
With others who'll commemorate our victory in the Baltic.
Try her for what you can: some trade like milliner
Or service as a kitchen maid. No contact.
Here's just a locket you can give her, two threads
Of grey and dark hair intertwined. My thanks.'
And clack of whip, and silent past Newgate.
'That's done. I'm sure she'll make her way.
It doesn't matter that he'll never know.'
The bundle's handed in. 'This dormitory here
With the others. And, for peace, mix gin
In their milk, nurse, won't you? It makes them quieter.'
Another lot baptized. The warden shuts the door,
Listens an instant to their mewling cries.
Footsteps echo in an empty corridor.

XIII: THE ATLANTIC.
OFF CAPE TRAFALGAR. *REDOUBTABLE*

Breezes so light they would not stir a woman's bonnet-ribbons;
Smoke from Conil up the coast still hanging in the air,
Thank God. The first time in a ship to Martinique I thought I'd die
Of fright and thirst upon this heaving, sucking element.
How I longed for the reassuring prattle
Of the marketplace, those sturdy mangers
Where the men lent, bargaining.
Not so bad these last weeks in Cadiz –
Some chance to get on land, go drinking,
Meet the women. Old Lucas keeps us practising
At targets, and it's no worry now to climb
The rigging as the sailors do. My favourite place
Is on the mizzenmast; there you've got
The whole quarterdeck covered with your musket
And in such little roll it's almost as steady
As a parade ground.
                                    Of course I'm nervous;
You've got to be if you want to call yourself
A crack marksman. That's the skill:
To be so much keyed-up that you're a cat
Upon its prey, immobile, watching, waiting
For the inattention, all your being focused
Forward on the unsuspecting animal who turns
And turns again upon his little patch of ground.
Alerte! West upon the swell! A yellow and black colossus
With all sail possible upon her masts and bearing down!
Get to it! Stand across her! Hold!
Close in. Close in. Right upon our port she slides,
Her anchors forked tongues against the sky.
Far out in the Atlantic the ocean begins
To come alive and boom. Up here,
One seagull full across my wake
And blinking eye sheers down.
Victory closes on us with an orca's grace.

XIV: The Thames Estuary.
Greenwich

The last stretch. Past Cliffe, St George's pennant
Flashing above the marshes. Greenhythe, Gravesend
Arching her church buttresses over an ocean
To Chesapeake Bay, and then haul up
To Purfleet to await the tide. Coalfreighters
And tobacco ships jostle in the reaches,
Lightermen like larvae skim beneath the boats.
'Hoy up there! What's your cargo?'
Rum, saltpetre, sugar cane.
'That one's for Wapping': the sickly scent
Of bound humanity seeping from her hold.
Here's coffee, porcelaine for London's boudoirs,
Herring out of Lowestoft, cinnamon from Bengal
Lascars and Tonkininen shivering in the sleet.
'Let's get her up, men.' The tide's begun to turn.
Thames lifts herself upon the Atlantic
And bellies towards the city under blusterous rain.
Life current, sighing in creeks and reedbeds,
Past clacking mills and the arsenal's great guns
At Woolwich that now ram the air.
'Row, boys! We row him home to glory!
Look over there to Blackwall, the ribcages that'll be our Navy
Looming above the taverns, the hubbub
In the dockyards as they see us pass!'
This is the press of vantage: a cathedral
Of masts and sail that floats around the citadel
And through whose gates the sad and multitudinous peoples roar.
On the isle of dykes, weatherboard topples upon stilts of slime
And forges rage along the waterfront, their anvils
Chorusing out God's offices: wealth and toil.

Imperium

Rest oars. Gently to the landing stage.
This is the dead meridian of the world,
Measure which puts us at the centre of all that is.
Place him upon the rostra. Massive,
The territories hang in painted halls.

O Britannia, o gentes.

In on the tide rushes empire
Life-chord to Europe's dark heart.

D. J. Taylor & Philip Hensher
On Experimentalism

An email exchange

----**Original Message**----
From: D. J. Taylor <david@penandinc.co.uk>
To: Philip Hensher <philip@penandinc.co.uk>
Date: 19 June 2002 21:37
Subject: Experiment

Dear Philip,

I've always been wary of the idea of 'movements' in literature, generally believing that books get written in more mundane ways than the textbooks say they do, but it seems fair to say that the last year or so has seen some vague stirrings in the 'experimental' strain of British fiction. There was James Kelman's last novel, with the section that looked as if it had been produced by an exploding typewriter. The BS Johnson oeuvre is being reissued with a forthcoming biography by Jonathan Coe, and there is Coe's own last novel with its 13,000 word sentence. Usually, when these kind of ghosts get chased out of the not very extensive corner they occupy in modern Eng lit, I find myself thinking several things: 1) that any piece of writing worth its salt is, in some degree, experimental – *Vanity Fair* is an experiment, *A Dance to the Music of Time* is an experiment; 2) that the whole thing is an excuse for some not very worthwhile nostalgia about the 1960s experimental movement in the UK that included such writers as Eva Figes, Alan Burns, Ann Quinn and so on; 3) that many of the novels I admire most in twentieth-century British fiction incorporate elements of formal experiment in their work –

67

Firbank, Henry Green, early Anthony Powell, etc; 4) that even the staidest reactionaries of the modern novel can be found unexpectedly mucking about – sometimes very fruitfully – with the form, for example the dialogue in *Lucky Jim*.

Three things I'd particularly like your opinion on:

1 – What do we mean by an 'experimental novel'? After all, I noted one or two critics locating such a strain in your own last one and I'd never noticed it (in the sense hat they meant) myself.

2 – The American equivalent to our 1960s and 1970s movement – *Barth, Hawkes, Gass*, etc – always seemed to make a great deal more noise, and many of them are still going. But surely one can't take seriously someone like John Hawkes who declared, with apparent seriousness, that 'plot was the enemy of the novel'?

3 – Eva Figes once said that she wrote in the way she does because the English social realist tradition could never accommodate the horrors that had happened in her lifetime. Faber, the brainy anti-Lawrentian, anti-sentiment, anti-'stories' AS Byatt's *Still Life* says much the same about his own work. Can one only confront some terrible atrocity or cataclysm by coming at it from an angle, at any rate one in which the form can sometimes seem to take over from the content?

Yours

David

----**Original Message**----
From: Philip Hensher <philip@penandinc.co.uk>
To: D. J. Taylor <david@penandinc.co.uk>
Sent: Sunday, June 23, 2002 1:59 PM
Subject: Re: Experiment

Dear David,

Of course, you are right to say that all good novels are to some degree experimental, just as all novels, good or bad, deal in abstract ideas. Still, we know roughly what we mean when we talk about an 'experimental' novel, or a 'novel of ideas', so let's limit it artificially. It seems to me that there is a line to be drawn between the sort of novel which expects the reader to take some interest in the circumstances of the novel's making, and the sort whose art and formal decisions are essentially invisible. Of course, those are not hard distinctions; *Middlemarch* and *Tom Jones* enter into discussions of the novelist's art from time to time, as well as *Tristram Shandy*. But it might be a good place to start.

It's tempting to try and distinguish between novelists who experiment on the local, linguistic level, and those whose experiments are formal. In English especially, there are a large number of novelists who are happy to fill very orthodox forms with experimental sentences; most of Henry Green falls into this category, and Wyndham Lewis, looked at coldly, is no more of a structural innovator than Arnold Bennett. There are, too, a fair number of writers who wrote books in very unorthodox forms without ever moving far from an idealized, classical English – *Typhoon*, *The Man Who Was Thursday* or the best of Waugh.

Do these count as experimental novels? Certainly, when you get to the moment in *Typhoon* when you realize that the second storm has been omitted, it is a formal shock, and you feel the audacity of the tale. But high-period experimental fiction rests, rather, on a set of formal decisions which appear to be arbitrary. There is no particular reason, as far as I can see, why a book like Walter Abish's *Alphabetical Africa* should be structured like that; the first chapter contains only words beginning with A, the second A and B, the third A, B and C, and so on. Much of the Brooke Rose/BS Johnson corpus seems similarly arbitrary to me, and I wonder what the point of it really is.

Formal experimentation, really, needs some kind of rationale behind it. Georges Perec's *La Disparition* absolutely isn't arbitrary, in its decision to write entirely without the letter 'e'; it is really about Perec's big subject, the annihilation of European Jewry, and suggests that an entire strand of European civilization could be quietly removed without anyone subsequently noticing, just as no reviewer at the time noticed the single strange fact about the book. That is a very powerful metaphor, and the opposite of arbitrary. The 'experimental' novelist I like very much now is

On Experimentalism

Richard Beard, whose books arc all very rigidly organized, but in order to make a serious point. The last of them, *The Cartoonist*, is heartbreaking in its way; he wrote a scurrilous first draft, set in Euro-Disney, and then submitted it to libel lawyers. The final text is written strictly according to their requirements. It looks like an arbitrary way to write a book, but in the end it is saying something very direct about the relationship between power and words.

The trouble with many of the books you mention is that they strike me as, unlike Beard or Perec, basically arbitrary in their formal decisions. It looks like a sophisticated level to work at, but it would be truer to say that they are the slightly rudimentary work of someone slightly nervous. I think it all comes down to pre-determined schemes. If you teach creative writing, beginning novelists are always turning up with fantastically elaborate and rigidly-schemed books, and it takes some effort to persuade them to relax a little. And one frequently reads novels where it is apparent that the author has made a rigid rule for him or herself, very early on, and will stick to it even if it damages the material. Jonathan Buckley wrote a novel, *The Ghost Macindoe* (2001), which was not bad at all, but he'd made the firm decision to write one chapter for each year of his hero's life; by halfway through, you could sense that his rule was making it impossible for him to improvise, to move naturally, to say what he wanted to say. On a much smaller level, I thought John Lanchester really damaged the possibilities of *Mr Phillips* by the single, early decision that the hero was never going to be called anything but 'Mr Phillips'; it disastrously cramped some potentially moving scenes late in the book. The *locus classicus* here is Anthony Burgess's absolutely dire *Napoleon Symphony*; it probably seemed like quite a good idea at first to tell the life of Napoleon according to the implied narrative in Beethoven's *Eroica* symphony. The trouble comes when he gets to the third chapter, and finds that he's somehow required to write a scherzo and trio. For some reason, when faced with a choice between chucking the scheme or wrecking the novel, novelists always end up wrecking the novel.

There's an instructive comparison here. It seems to me that Austen in *Emma* and James in *What Maisie Knew* made pretty well the same decision, that the action would all take place in the presence of a single character. James sticks rigidly to his rule, and I think it starts to damage the book – the second half is just exhausting. Austen in general sticks to the rule, but from time to time, she does see that there are things Emma can't overhear, and the convention is occasionally broken.

Experimental fiction, I think, is all too often rather like this, conforming to a pre-determined scheme, rather than, as one would wish, moving through improvisation and speculation. Experimental fiction, I feel, ought to be more like *Vile Bodies*. What it usually resembles is the *Napoleon Symphony*, which ought to act as a grim warning. No one, after all, would pay to see an escapologist chain himself up.

No, I don't know why anyone thought any of my novels were remotely experimental. I wondered whether anyone who said that had read much in the way of the nineteenth-century classics – there wasn't much in *The Mulberry Empire* which would have surprised the reader of *Vanity Fair* or *The Woman in White*. The things people found alarming, I think, were the fragmentary and inconclusive narratives, the element of pastiche and the running patter of allusion. I found it hard to believe that anyone who had read (in order) *War and Peace*, Proust or Milton would find anything very novel about any of this. As far as I know, that is just how books are written.

Yours ever

Philip

----**Original Message**----
From: D. J. Taylor <david@penandinc.co.uk>
To: Philip Hensher <philip@penandinc.co.uk>
Date: 24 June 2002 15:01
Subject: Re: Experiment

Dear Philip,

The distinction you make between the kind of book where the

reader is expected to take an interest in the formal proceedings and the kind where everything happens invisibly seems to be well worth making. Beetle-browed formalism always seems faintly alarming, as well as often leaving the human bits of the book some distance behind. Isn't Leavis, when asked to compare Joyce and Shakespeare, supposed to have said that the one was labouring to extend the limits of the form while the other worked under the pressure of something to be conveyed?

The formal experimenters – which in this country seems to mean that 1960s lot, several of whom are still with us – often seem to be locked in a fairly predictable artistic pattern where you sometimes feel that better effects could be achieved without the sleight of hand. I read the re-issue of Johnson's *The Unfortunates* – the one served up in discrete sections in a feeling that on the one hand it contained passages of startling beauty, and on the other that a more reliable form would have done more for the things Johnson was trying to say. The same sensation was levied by that Rayner Heppenstall novel, *Two Moons*, which you can read on all the left-handed and right-handed pages or sequentially depending on how you feel. But why? I feel the same about the language as language is spoken patter of, say, Eva Figes. No doubt three-year-olds do articulate in the manner of the one in her last novel ('Rosey, posey, nosey,' etc, etc), but one would rather listen to one's own three-year-old doing it.

But one can see formal technical advances colonizing the mainstream. In small doses, I've always greatly admired Firbank's novels. Here he seems to me: 1) to have refined the 'talking heads' convention to a superior degree, to the point where one can distinguish individual speech without the 'He said', 'She said' prefixes; 2) to have coined a kind of vivid impressionist shorthand (for example: the Mouth family's journey to Cuna-Cuna by jolting cart in *Prancing Nigger* is rendered simply as 'Little jingley trot trot over the wide savannah' – hey!); and 3) to have been able to advance the plot simply by dialogue, as in the stuff about fleas infesting the Ritz Hotel in *The Flower Beneath The Foot*. Waugh specifically uses this in the events leading up to Lord Tangent's death after the Llanabba sports in *Decline and Fall*.

On the other hand, no one could say that Firbank was

constrained by the experimentalist straitjacket – he was simply using words in the way he thought best. Some of the work I admire from that period – or slightly later – seems to make its effects by pastiching conventional narratives of the time. For example, Anthony Powell's *From A View To A Death* – one of his very best books – is a send-up of the country house novel, just as *Venusberg* is a send-up of the young man abroad novel. And yet – I take your point about localized experiment – each can be seen in relatively conventional 'English' terms.

To move forward to the here and now, one is often invited to see an experimental tang in the vernacular – or, if you ask me, mock-vernacular – stuff that emanates from north of the border and other places. But Welsh and co. seem to me about as formally experimental and innovative as Galsworthy.

Best

David

----Original Message----
From: Philip Hensher <philip@penandinc.co.uk>
To: D. J. Taylor <david@penandinc.co.uk>
Sent: Tuesday, June 25, 2002 10:48 PM
Subject: Re: Experiment

Dear David,

Phew – at last I find something to disagree with you about. I rather feared that this was going to develop into a Marsh-Marlowe correspondence between two superannuated Young Fogeys – a condition perhaps not obviously different from being an old fogey. The thing I do disagree with you about is the idea that, in reality, there is any distinction to be made between the artificiality of the artistic conventions in high realism, and those of high modernism. In my view, what you call 'something to be conveyed' passes through linguistic and aesthetic conventions in seemingly transparent 'realist' texts in exactly the same way as in opaque 'modernist' texts. That is, if there is any 'something to be conveyed', any 'out-there', any *'dehors-du-texte'* (to quote a now rather period thinker) at all. My general view is that there is, in fact, nothing there but prose, even if some writers are more dedicated to the ingeniously contrived illusion than others.

The distinction I made is not an original one, but Anthony Burgess's. Burgess's distinction was in part a false one, based on a naive notion of intention, and he seems to distinguish between writers who are 'interested in language' and writers who are not Personally, I think all good writers are interested in language and form, but only some of them expect their readers to share this interest, which is a slightly different matter. The virtue I would claim for experimental writers is that they do make the reader conscious of the fact that even in the most apparently transparent realist novels, conventions exist and artificial decisions have been made. That randomly ordered BS Johnson novel does make one think retrospectively, about the conventions of *entrelacement* in any classic novel. For me, the novels of I. Compton-Burnett have been an incisive influence whenever I think about the conventions of speech in a novel, and the last six novels of Henry James, from *The Awkward Age* to *The Golden Bowl* – a series which for me goes further in codifying the technical principles of fiction than anything else in English – make one pause before writing a word, and think abstractly of style, commentary, point of view. Increasingly, I want to write something transparent and natural; the odd feeling I have is that one only attains this transparency by cold, analytical, technical control.

Yes, Firbank is interesting. There is a debate to be had here over novelists, like him, Henry Green, and I. Compton-Burnett who are experimentalists by default – I doubt whether any of them quite knew how experimental they were being. In each case it just seemed the natural way to write, rather than (as in the case of Joyce or Beckett) conscious efforts in a radical direction. I can never quite decide whether Firbank was a primitive, like the Douanier Rousseau, or *faux-naif*, and in any case, it isn't a very fruitful discussion to embark upon.

In any case, you do isolate an extremely valuable and pervasive theme among experimentalists, in the fleas in the Ritz in the

Flower Beneath The Foot. As you say, this turns harmlessly into Waugh's story of Lord Tangent's terrible decline. What followed that, of course, was one of Henry Green's favourite devices. Waugh complained loudly about the amputation story in *Nothing*, but Green is always doing that, putting the big tragic story at the margins of the novel. That sense that the real story is elsewhere is one of the key inventions of experimental fiction – it is true about *Ulysses*, *Mrs Dalloway*, the best of Hemingway, and dozens of other things up to *Rosencrantz and Guildenstern are Dead* and beyond. The *locus classicus* must be that sublime story of V.S. Pritchett's, *When My Girl Came Home*, where the real story only emerges in the final sentence.

I'm interested in this, since it does start to suggest that when fiction reaches a point of ultimate, artificial, rigid experimentation, it tends to evoke a reality which exists outside the text That is true about Kelman, *Pale Fire*, and even *Finnegan's Wake*. It's often said that high modernism refuses to admit any extra-linguistic reality, but I wonder if that is true. A book like *Pale Fire* seems to me to depend on an evocation of and a faith in a narrative, an existence outside these hardbacked words which is nowhere perceptible in Tolstoy or George Eliot. It reinforces my sense that experimental literature is in a sense not more advanced, but more primitive than the high realists.

As you know, I am rather interested in the questions of inter-textual debates you raise, and am interested in the question of when a book passes from an *example* of a genre to a commentary on it. In the case of the country house novel, we can talk about *Crome Yellow*, *A View To A Death*, *Loving*, *Brideshead Revisited*, *Love in a Cold Climate*, *In A Summer Season*, and on to *Atonement*. In each case, is it a commentary or simply an example? Should one not be extremely wary of the academic tendency to claim that an ironic, disenchanted version of a genre has a merit above an embodiment of that genre? This may in some cases be true, but I myself don't see that a work which contains an ironic commentary on its own generic conventions is necessarily more profound than a straight embodiment of those conventions – a self-aware campus novel, like David Lodge's *Small World*, rather than a transparent one like Jane Smiley's *Moo*, at the lowest level.

On Experimentalism

It seems kinder not to talk about Welsh. I suppose you could regard him as doing something original if you were entirely unaware of the long-established conventions of Lallans, and if you had never read one of Dickens' death-bed scenes. No, as I say, kinder not to.

Yours ever

Philip

----**Original Message**----
From: D. J. Taylor <david@penandinc.co.uk>
To: Philip Hensher <philip@penandinc.co.uk>
Date: 29 June 2002 15:09
Subject: Re: Experiment

Dear Philip,

Alas, I don't think I do disagree with you about there being any distinction between the artificiality of the conventions of high realism and those of high modernism, naturalism or anything else. For example, reading some of the 'dirty realist' fiction promoted on these shores since the mid-1980s, I'm forever conscious that most of it seems to have originated in the creative writing school. Annie Proulx, for instance, seems a fantastically mannered writer even down to the clunking determinism and the silly names – no one, even in Wyoming, could possibly be called 'Leecil Lee'. Didn't they discover among Raymond Carver's papers draft upon carefully finessed draft of those minimalist short stories hailed at the time of publication for their authenticity, and so on? Scratch an *echt-realist* and something altogether rococo often emerges from beneath. I'm just re-reading an ancient Stan Barstow novel and struck by the weirdness of the narrative conventions, attempts to render down everyday 'thought' into prose and so on.

Going back to naturalism, in its classic sense – to me perhaps best exemplified by all those sprawling early twentieth-century

Americans – it seems that some of the most fruitful forms of experiment come when a writer brings elements of a different discipline to the idea of those unappeasable but not necessarily malign (just inevitable) forces that preside over life. I was always very struck, reading Steinbeck's *The Grapes of Wrath* – one of those novels that somehow defy every one of the limitations that criss-cross their surface – of the way in which Steinbeck brings in his training as a marine biologist to convey an idea of people swarming like insects across the face of America. In fact, Steinbeck seems a good example of a way in which a writer can attach all kinds of passing 'experimental' conventions to what starts off as a realistic novel to cunning effect – for example, the sudden switch to first-person narration by detached onlookers like the car salesman; or stray vignettes like the account of the roadside diner on Route 66.

But what about Firbank and co.? I think there's something in the idea of the primitive who is just doing what he or she does regardless of intellectual goading from elsewhere. I recently read Anthony Hobson's edition of F's letters to his mother, in which he shows evidence of practically no interior landscape at all, apart from an obsession with money and not being bored. BS Johnson was much more of a theorist but you sense a kind of doggedness, a man driven by the conviction that of a vast marching army he is the only one in step.

Thinking about this, and the earlier remarks about naturalism, I wonder whether it could be said that 'primitives' are sometimes at their best in those blood-coloured determinist homelands. For me the moment when that 'ultimate rigid point of experimentation' you talk about, when something can be glimpsed outside whatever is going on in the text tends to occur in writers like, say, Hardy or Theodore Dreiser. Dreiser is a fantastic example of a writer who, according to the standard yardsticks, can't write, but who by labouring on in his particular style turns practically baroque. For example, the passages in *An American Tragedy* where Clyde Griffiths kills his pregnant girlfriend without really meaning to, which are a kind of endless prose poem. Hardy, too, ('genius but no talent', Virginia Woolf suggested) seems to end up by offering almost formalist pastiches of himself (*Two on a Tower* et cetera). Incidentally, Anthony Powell always reckoned that Firbank borrowed some of his dialogue effects from Hardy's rustics.

All the best

David

----**Original Message**----
From: Philip Hensher <philip@penandinc.co.uk>
To: D. J. Taylor <david@penandinc.co.uk>
Sent: Tuesday, June 25, 2002 10:48 PM
Subject: Re: Experiment

Dear David,

We are slightly getting off the point of departure here, but I must say that my point about realism resting on artificial conventions was by no means intended to denigrate it. It is true that there is a peculiar magic in writers, like Defoe or Tolstoy, whose calculations are more or less invisible, but it is not really a criticism of a realist writer to say that his or her workings are occasionally visible to the attentive render, surely?

That, surely, comes close to the heart of the matter of what I myself perceive as a proper aim for the novel. The novel, I think, exists between two pure ideals. The first is the novel of unmodified abstract form; the second is the novel of unmediated life. I feel that the closer a novel grows towards one or other of these ideals, the more desiccated an appearance it presents to its readers. The experimental novel, proceeding in the grip of explicit form, is at the one extreme; the novel of rambling, shapeless existence (Dorothy Richardson, say) at the other. For me, the most moving and impressive moments of the great novels come when one predominant mode suddenly yields to its opposite; when a strictly ordered novel gives a glimpse of untidy human experience, like the climaxes of *Ulysses*, or when one suddenly glimpses a rigid, formal move in a realist chronicle.

What I have in mind are the resolution when Becky Sharp gives Amelia Sedley a letter, the classical recapitulation of Darcy's second proposal, or that superb short story by Chekhov, 'Dr Startsev', where a perfectly realist narrative suddenly starts repeating itself in every single respect. These moments of yielding are, I think, what the novel ought to aim at. When the experimental novel shrinks from any engagement with unshaped experience, or the realist from any moment of explicit artifice or revealed form, I think it sacrifices a great deal.

Of course, this is an extraordinarily difficult balance to strike. Nor is it a problem confined to 'high' literature: when a thriller sticks too closely to the conventions of its genre, we will find it banal; when it ventures too far from them, we will find it incoherent. But you have to keep trying, and not to pin your colours too firmly to the mast of one or other unattainable ideal. For myself, I've always tried to render existence, but also to give the reader glimpses of the workings of the machine; in *The Mulberry Empire*, say, to see if it was possible to make a reader cry over a figure in a pastiche. I don't have any doubt that the great experimental novels open up all sorts of possibilities, but, in almost every case, they have done so by limiting their own reach. Very particular technical points are demonstrated by *What Maisie Knew*, *Jacob's Room*, Firbank, Compton-Burnett, Robbe-Grillet, BS Johnson, Perec, Calvino and all the rest, but the purity of the demonstration, however useful, was in each case not enough to make a great work of art, and they must be justified by their eclectic and rebellious students. *Tristram Shandy* is a remarkable consideration of something no one had ever thoroughly investigated before, the question of what is the proper ratio in a literary narrative of words to time. Sterne made every thoughtful writer subsequently consider the propriety, or the possibility of devoting 10,000 words to the events of one hour, or dismissing a year in a page, but he only raised a question which he could not answer. No one would approach point-of-view instinctively after *What Maisie Knew*, which proves a point but it remains a brilliant postulate, a theory only to receive authoritative endorsement with *Zauberberg* and *A La Recherche du Temps Perdu*, like those speculations of Max Planck and Einstein regarding the behaviour of the physical universe which could not be observed until technology was able to construct microscopes and telescopes of sufficient power.

So, in my view, the experimental novel, even at its most inspired, almost never results in a truly satisfying aesthetic experience. But I would rather like to sign off, given the generally negative tone I seem to have adopted until now, with a positive observation, and say that the best experimentalists have always made things happen, even with fundamentally unsatisfactory and incomplete works. It strikes me, looking at the incomplete list I just made, of good and admirable experimentalists, that they do this when they codify and specify aspects of the novel which were always lying there, unconsidered – James's investigations of point-of-view, Compton-Burnett's establishment of an entirely linguistic universe, Calvino's conflations of Fate and formal narrative necessity. More recently, Alan Hollinghurst's *The Swimming-Pool Library* did something which everyone needs to ponder, though most readers didn't even notice it: what would a novel look like if it contained absolutely no female characters whatsoever? All these endeavours are worth something, although I think they could have become bigger if they had at some point decisively broken the rule they had established – what an entrance a woman could have made, fifty pages from the end of *The Swimming-Pool Library*! What dramatic force would be contained in a sudden physical description of the weather lasting a page, in the penultimate chapter of *Manservant and Maidservant*! But these, nevertheless, are useful and instructive books. When a novelist's experiments, on the other hand, demonstrate nothing but an arbitrary and meretricious virtuosity, and offers no general principles from which lessons may be learnt, I rather think it is not worth very much.

The difference is between *Tristram Shandy* and another novel of the 1760s, much celebrated at the time, Charles Johnstone's *Chrysal*, which is a vast epic, almost entirely narrated by a coin as it passes from pocket to pocket. Sterne has lasted because he pointed something out which no one had ever quite noticed, and which subsequently everyone has had to consider. Johnstone disappeared because the only circumstances in which a novelist could learn from him is if he proposed to write a novel narrated by an inanimate object. Yes, I know, every so often someone does write a novel with an inanimate narrator – wasn't there a boy who wrote a book the other day with a supermarket trolley for a hero? Worse than that, I once had someone in a creative writing class who wrote an entire novel from the point-of-view of a plank of wood. (Well, not quite – at first the narrator was A Tree in the Forest before tragedy struck and the narrator was chopped down, thereby condemning all the human action – seduction, marriages, funerals, the works, to take place in a timber yard. His name was Reg. His prospects were few.) But for novels with inanimate narrators, novels in the form of palindromes, novels in which every single chapter is exactly 1000 words long, there is no hope. Because in each case there is no truth, no fundamental and necessary truth in that.

All the best

Philip

image: monkeyfrog - gary dylan seal
<gds@mcpoetry.co.uk>

Andy Brown
Taxidermy

Katya and Daniel sit in silence, staring at their reflections. The humming bird cabinet throws back the colours of their jackets and jeans like the blush of stained glass. Beyond their mute reflections, the stuffed birds stare back, their thin claws gripping the lichened twigs under glowing crests and streamers: the Spatuletail, the Amethyst Woodstar, the Frilled Coquette.

'I've bought everything for supper,' he finally murmurs.

'Uh-huh?'

'I thought I'd cook, then we could . . .'

'What?'

'You know . . .'

'Did you?' She says.

'We haven't for ages.' A long pause. 'Katya . . .?'

Katya digs a fingernail into the soft pad between his forefinger and thumb. An electric pulse passes all the way up Daniel's arm, from wrist to humerus. 'Can't you think of anything else?' She says. 'C'mon. Let's go.'

They stride past the Ichthyosaurs into the main hall. Light struggles through the high windows. Katya cranes her neck to the domes of the ceiling, but twists it painfully in doing so. She smoothes her palm towards her nape as they pass beneath the arching bones of Diplodocus, its rib cage rising like the vaults of a cathedral. They file through the turnstiles and out of the main doors, stepping into the fresh air, along the sweeping curve of the driveway and out through the railings.

'Strange out here,' she says, 'after all that taxidermy.'

'You can't prove that all *this* isn't just stuffing,' he replies, throwing his arms wide in an arc at passers by. 'Not for sure.'

They walk around the corner and down into the subway, where streams of office workers stride purposefully to the trills and arpeggios of a busker's clarinet. The woodwind carries to the other end of the tunnel. On the train, the only people speaking are the tourists. Everyone avoids each other's eyes. Daniel reaches for Katya's hand and holds it tentatively, but she pulls it away to fiddle with the buttons of her coat. Once more they stare at their reflections. A curve in the glass distorts their heads beyond all recognition.

Katya and Daniel have only recently moved in together; an attempt to be 'more together' – his idea – after years of separate living. They can't really afford it, but the flat is nice enough in a curious way to keep them living there – the bedroom is reached by a ladder, on a high balcony that surveys a ring of sofas set around a table. This evening, the table is strewn with Katya's work: designs for an expensive townhouse garden. The walls of the flat need a coat of paint – something he has promised he'll 'deal with' – but the damp is mostly hidden behind paintings and photos and shelves piled high, so there's no real rush he argues.

They sit apart on the sofas, her hand picking at strands of coloured candle wax from the encrusted neck of a wine bottle. She rolls the strands between her finger and thumb, warming them into pliable pellets. He suspends a sugar cube on a teaspoon, letting it slowly dissolve into the mud-brown coffee.

'D'you have to make that mess?' He asks carelessly.

'It's only wax for god's sake.' She grips her top lip between her teeth and lets her shoulders rise.

He tilts his head boyishly, like a puppy hoping for forgiveness and lifts his coffee cup, draining it off. A milky line of froth appears along his upper lip. She indicates it with a nod and he licks at it, asking her if it has gone. She nods and flicks the hair off her brow.

Has he always been like this, she thinks, and she has simply failed to notice it; or is it her reading things negatively when everything, in fact, is fine? They stare dully at each other for a second. Her hand reaches for the wax again, but she catches his eye and lets her hand fall slowly to the table, drumming an erratic rhythm. Across the table, his face has begun to merge into shadow.

'It's not just me is it?' she asks. 'You can feel it too can't you? Daniel?'

'Shall I cook?' He asks.

'Don't avoid it Daniel!' She shouts, 'Don't avoid me! Just think about it.'

'I do,' he says. 'All the time.'

'You know, sometimes I feel as though we live in completely different worlds. For a few minutes we're joined to each other, then we're . . .' she searches for the words, 'fumbling in the darkness . . .'

'Uh-huh,' he nods, rubbing his eyebrow and turning to the sink.

'I'm going to have a bath,' she says.

While Katya bathes, he starts preparing dinner. She finally comes out of the bathroom in her maroon robe.

'Jesus, how much stuff did you buy this morning?' she asks. The table groans under its load: a pot filled with seafood – crab, shrimps, fish and clams – market bargains he hunted down earlier in the morning.

'I wanted oysters, but they were out. I wanted to make you a nice meal, ' he says, reaching for her arm. He pulls her back into him, burying his face in the crook of her neck, but she slips away to open the fridge.

'That's nice,' she says, 'but pasta would have done.'

He reaches out to the fridge and yanks open the door in front of her, twisting the cap off a bottle of beer. He sips at it, staring at the stainless steel door, a smear of grease blemishing its otherwise polished surface.

'Right, well next time I won't bother then,' he says.

'I didn't mean it like that,' she says.

'Well how did you mean it, Katya?' He asks.

'I didn't mean it in any particular way. You know, if we talked a little more, you'd know,' she says.

'Well we *could* talk more if you were here a bit more often,' he says. 'You haven't exactly been around much recently.'

'What do you mean *around*? I haven't been away anywhere for months!' Then, more quietly, 'Feels like years sometimes.'

'You know what I mean,' he says. 'You've not been here, not really.' He taps his temple with his finger.

'Daniel, we've been through this *so* many times. I've got work to finish, to pay for this . . .' she gestures around the flat, 'as you keep reminding me. All this was your idea, anyway.'

'I know, I know.' He rubs his shoulder with his cheek.

'It does you good to spend time on your own. It never hurt you in the past.' She finds herself starting the next sentence hardly having thought about it. 'Anyway, we haven't been making enough space for each other recently. It'll help us decide where to go next.'

He looks surprised, as though she's about to tell him it's all over.

'There isn't anything to decide on, is there?'

'No, I was just . . .' She goes quiet, fumbling for an end to the sentence, but it spills away from her like a blob of mercury; disintegrating, particulate. The pause tugs at them both like a vacuum. 'Can't we just eat?' She asks, picking up a fresh shrimp, pink as a marshmallow, and twisting off its head.

'Fine,' he says. 'It's ready whenever.'

Supper over, they start to wash the dishes. She piles the bowls together in the sink. He rises and shuffles across the flat. She watches him slowly climb the ladder.

'I'll do it by myself then,' she says sarcastically. 'Again!'

'Leave it. I'll do it in the morning. Let's go to bed,' he urges.

'It'll stink,' she says. 'Go on.' Her voice drops in resignation as she sinks her hands into the foaming suds.

At the top of the stairs he makes a satisfied guttural noise and leans over the banister. She turns to see his face peering down like a corbel, high on a wooden column in a church.

The dishes done, Katya climbs the ladder and finds him lying on the edge of the bed in the lamplight, wrapped in a blanket, smoking a cigarette. The lingering odour of seafood hangs in the air with his smoke; a cloud that swirls about them in layers, like Saturn's rings. A line of glass bottles on the bedstead reflects the star-point tip of his cigarette.

A minute later, she is sitting up in her striped nightshirt. She can see him side-glancing at the shadow of her cleavage, aroused, trailing his eye across her stomach and down her legs. She has one foot tucked beneath a thigh, the other foot pulled sideways so that she can scratch its sole with a small file.

'Do you have to?' He says.

'It's a rough patch.'

'You're telling me,' he says. She looks at him with contempt. 'But in the bed?'

'Fine. I'll stop.' She gives in, pushing her back against the board, tucking her toes under the covers. 'It's not as bad as *smoking* in bed.'

He draws deeply, exhales and stubs the cigarette out in the ashtray. Then he lunges across the bed and makes to snatch the file away from her. He misses and catches her hand.

'Do you mind,' she says, indicating his grip on her wrist. He lets her go.

'For god's sake! Look at us. It feels like we're in a fucking Beckett play.'

'And what does that mean?'

'You know what it means . . .'

She reaches up to her hair and removes a clip, letting it fall out of its topknot. It curtains her liquid brown eyes. He leans across the bed and flips the switch on the stereo. Classical music slips from the speakers. The niggling moments of the evening begin to fade away. He reaches over and coaxes her towards him.

'I'm sorry,' he whispers, starting to rub her shoulders in a smooth massage. He kneads her neck like a potter working clay, rhythmically lifting his hands in a motion that make a vessel of her back, a spout of her neck, releasing pressure from her softest points; releasing the twist she had put in it earlier. She lolls her head from side to side. He goes on rubbing her neck with one hand, as his other slips around her front and brushes its way across her belly towards the warmth between her legs.

'Slowly,' she complains, pulling away from him. 'My neck was enjoying that.' He bangs his head against her back several times.

'Sorry. I thought we . . .' He waits a moment. 'I'll do your back,' he promises.

'It's too late now,' she says, reaching over to the music and turning it low. 'Just slow down. Why can't you just take it as it comes?'

He wants to argue, but knows it will do no good. Instead he sinks back into silence and switches off the light. They lie still in the darkness a moment longer, the space between them growing larger with every breath. He waits, then moves his arm to drape around her shoulder. His nose nudges along the flat expanse to the base of her neck, some soft exposed skin, up to the depths of her ear, secret like a honeycomb. She shrugs and turns her back to him. They lie like spoons.

Late in the night, she sits up, her eyes tracing vague movements of light across the ceiling. She has been thinking too much. She can't sleep. She can't actually think about anything of importance. Daniel turns in his sleep. She twists her legs from under the duvet, gathers her dressing gown around her, and slips out of bed. He stirs, dreaming of a world where sex is always fulfilled and fulfilling, sweet, uncomplicated and resolved. He grunts and snuffles, before lolling onto his back, his eyes opening to reveal two slits of white, tinged red by alcohol. She goes down the ladder to the sofa and switches on the television, turning the volume low.

Katya shifts on her haunches, bringing her elbows to rest on the tabletop. Her fingers crown her head, interlocking through her hair. A slim shaft of moonlight bounces back off the underside of the balcony and hits the glass table top beneath her elbows. Her thoughts follow its path up and across the room, out of a high window like a bird on the wing of a dream. She rolls her head, slowly at first to relax her neck, then faster and faster, to tempt herself into the waiting void of sleep. Upstairs, he turns over noisily in bed. She pulls her legs up onto the sofa and lets her head fall onto one shoulder, like a barn owl watching, waiting.

'Tomorrow,' she whispers to herself.

Upstairs, she can hear him snoring erratically. Oblivious. Man in an ecstasy of creation.

Carol Birch
Turn Again Home

An extract

Morland was heaven, Gorton was home: the greyhound racing at Belle Vue; the buses going up and down Hyde Road; the Essoldo and the baths and the trains at Gorton Tank and the Beyer, Peacock siren going off every night at six; Ryder Brow and Old Hall Drive and Sunnybrow Park in the valley, with the swings and the roundabout and the Witch's Hat, and the old ladies with fat legs sitting on benches; and small yellow caterpillars with beady black dots on their backs moving everywhere over the wrinkled nearly black bark of the creaky old trees round the sides. You collected them and kept them in a jam-jar with leaves and twigs and watched them crawl about.

Over the railway, into the wilds – where gypsies camped on Mellands, the big fields that went on into open country of beck and gorse and hillock all the way to Reddish. In the daytime boys played football and girls played rounders on the edge. If you walked by their camp, the rough dark gypsy men and little dirty children all looked, the women with hair piled on top, tied up with bits of bright rag. The skinny brown dogs barked at Jock. After dark you saw the campfires. You smelt the horses and the smoke.

They weren't allowed to play on Mellands when the gypsies were there, but they did. Mam had a rhyme: *My mother said that I never should* . . . but the gypsy kids weren't friendly anyway. Still, Nell liked to see them there with their painted wagons and cooking pots, and all their lovely great horses grazing. She'd have given anything to have a horse to ride. But she wouldn't hobble her horse. That was cruel. The gypsy kids rode bareback and barefoot and roamed the roads, instead of staying in one place

89

like everybody else. Auntie Bennet roamed about too. But Nell had only ever lived in two places, first when they were all in one room together, Mam and Dad and Violet and Nell, and Bobby when he was a baby. Then here. When they moved in, the estate was so new it was still being built on cleared back-to-back slums like they still had in West Gorton and Longsight. They moved in – a real house! A semi with a front and back garden and a path up the side – and the builders built on next door for the next family.

By now the houses had settled into their foundations. Grass grew up between the flagstones.

They ate boiled egg and soldiers, the family at the table, kitchen door open, flies buzzing around the flypaper hanging there. Jock sat staring up at Dad with his ears pricked. Violet was at work – Saturday shift at the chocolate factory. Mam sliced the tops off the two eggs smartly, a no-nonsense chop. She and Dad had the tops with their bread and marg. Bobby and Nell got the good bits, the strong orange yolks to salt and dip their soldiers in and dunk up and down, the whites to scrape till the shells were completely clean but still intact, so that they could turn them upside down in the stripy egg-cups and pretend they were as good as new. It didn't work unless the shells were clean. You had to make sure the yolk didn't run down the shell. Dad hated that. He was very fastidious.

'I don't want my egg,' said Nell nonchalantly.

'Neither do I,' said Bob.

'Oh, an egg for me! Look Sam, our Bobby's giving me his egg!'

'Oh, what a good boy!'

'You can have mine, Dad,' said Nell, pushing her saucer towards him. It worked every time.

'Oh, that is kind! A nice fresh egg!'

Reaching for it, Dad's hands shook a little because of the war.

Mam and Dad made a great show of delight, cracking the lovely white eggs with their teaspoons; they made an even greater show of their disappointment, staring with open-mouthed disbelief at the shattered shells, faces falling in mock despair. The children shrieked with laughter. The little fluffy black dog ran about all over the place with its daft stump of a tail wagging like mad. Jock was a kind of Scottie who considered himself of equal status with the children. Dad stood, chuckling, a little man with even features, slight and pale with dark curling hair. He stood very erect because he was once a soldier, used to marching about and standing up straight on the parade ground. Upon the sideboard was the big framed picture of him taken in civvies when he was first discharged, Pte Samuel Bruce Holloway of the Labour Corps, with the ends of his moustache waxed, wavy hair slicked back and a cigarette in one hand. He sang a song to the tune of *What A Friend We Have In Jesus*.

When I get my civvy clothes on
No more soldiering for me . . .

it began, and it ended:

Then I will tell the sergeant-major
To stick his medals up his arse.

There weren't any photos of Mam.

Mam started nagging again as she cleared the table, 'I don't suppose you did their beds,' she said, 'Did you?' Mam's face was round and rosy, broad-nosed, with flat cheeks on which the veins were beginning to crack.

'I've put them in a bucket,' he muttered mysteriously, reaching for his cigarettes on the mantelpiece.

'You've what?' Stout in her flowery pinafore, she straightened; the tops of her arms wobbled.

'The sheets and pillow cases. I've put them in a bucket. They're soaking.' He struck a match.

'Well what's the bloody use of that if you haven't put fresh sheets on!'

'You sound like a parrot.'

'I'll give you parrot, you cheeky bugger, get upstairs and change them sheets now.'

'Give us a bit of peace, woman,' Dad said, crossing his legs, 'I've only just sat down.'

'It's alright for them as can!'

She stamped into the kitchen.

And so they went on, backwards and forwards as they endlessly did, until Dad stood up and gave Mam a look, raising his eyebrows and jerking his head towards the ceiling, and they both fell silent for a second.

Then she said, 'Bugger off.'

But they went upstairs anyway, for a lie-down.

Mam's litany: Don't touch the stove. Don't touch the plugs. Violet'll be home in a minute. And don't you pick on that lad!

'I don't pick on him!'

'You do,' said Bob.

'I don't!'

'You do.'

'Don't start,' said Mam and closed the door on them.

Bobby could act daft till the cows come home. He lay on the floor and wrestled with Jock, then got up onto his knees and pretended to be Al Jolson singing *Mammy* to Jinty the cat, which had got onto Dad's chair and was just settling down. Jinty completely ignored him.

'Ssh!' Nell said, kicking Bob, 'You'll have Mam down.'

He laughed and kicked back, turning his attention to Jock.

'Mammy!' He throbbed, 'Doncha know me? I'm ya liddle baby!'

Jock began to bark.

Bob hurled himself flat and wailed, 'Mammy! My liddle mammy!' Jock jumped on and off his head, shivering, till something beyond anyone else's senses distracted him and he started running frantically backwards and forwards between the door and the table, whimpering.

'Vi,' said Nell, getting up and opening the front door. The gate was ajar. Jock ran out and sat there wagging his tail, staring at the place at the top of the street where she would appear. When she did he was off like a bullet. Down she went with her arms out to catch him and wrestle his head. Vi had a drawn appearance round the eyes, hollow cheeks with prominent bones, a thin mouth. 'Good boy, Jock!' She cooed, 'Good little lad!' putting her hand down into her bag and bringing out a chocolate to pop in his mouth. She brought home bags of mis-shapes from the factory, dusty and delicious, making sure to get in a few of everyone's favourites – soft centres for Nelly, hard centres for Mam, Turkish Delight for Dad and soft caramels for Bob. Nobody liked coffee creams so they gave those to Jock.

Violet was in charge now. Vi was not their proper sister; she was only half. She threw herself down with her legs sprawling. 'Make us a cup of tea, Nell,' she said. It was good to have Vi back. She was so funny she could make them wet themselves laughing, with her funny faces and silly voices. Vi was no looker but her eyes had great humour and her hair was soft and dark and sat about her face in big sausagey curls. She turned the wireless on and sat tapping her feet and humming, playing with Jock and waiting for her tea, which she took black. 'Ooh ta, love. Hey, I met Uncle John. He's made one of his sponges, shall we go round? Hey, Auntie Bennet's been round Uncle Edmund's. He was dashing, so he didn't say too much.' Then she started laughing over some daft thing at work, but she couldn't tell them what it was because it wasn't quite suitable; only she would anyway because they wouldn't understand. Anyway: this girl, her little brother comes to meet her at the gates when they clocked off, and he's been to the dentist and had a tooth out so he's all bleeding round the mouth, poor little soul, and he's got this white thing over his mouth to catch the blood with two little loops one at either end, and he's got the loops one over each ear, and it's a – she leaned forward and whispered loudly, '– an S.T.!'

Nelly laughed.

'What's an S.T.?' Bobby asked.

'You're too young,' said Nell.

'Oh definitely!' Vi confirmed, 'Much too young.'

He flicked his fingers at them as if they were a couple of witches and aimed a kick towards their shins. Violet grabbed him and tickled him mercilessly, face set with glee. He screamed piercingly and Dad thumped on the ceiling.

They subsided in a flurry of shushing and giggling.

'Do a dance, Vi,' they begged, 'go on, do a dance.'

Violet twiddled the knob of the wireless till she got fast, jazzy music. Wide-eyed, side by side on the settee, they watched her skinny black-stockinged legs, twisting and writhing crazily in the frenzy of a made-up dance.

'More!' they cried each time she stopped, and she'd laugh and start all over again. When she was too exhausted to go on, she decided all at once to take them out, round to Uncle John and Auntie Grace's. 'Right!' She cried. 'That's enough of that, Vi! Come on! Let's go and get the news of Auntie Bennet!'

She'd been taking care of them for years, wiping their faces, hauling them around with her, putting on their coats and bonnets, pushing them up and down the street in the old pram, airing them and getting them out of the one room lodging in which they all used to live.

So she checked their hands and noses automatically.

Granny and Grandad had six sons and three daughters, and three of the sons lived on Sutton Estate: Dad, Uncle John and Uncle Edmund. Why, with an erudite, educated father who'd been a headmaster, did Sam and his brothers end up living on public assistance in grim old Gorton? Maybe it was the war. Maybe it was the things they hardly ever talked about. The Somme. Passchendaele. The trenches, the frostbite, the shaking hands. Or maybe it was the Holloway weakness, they all have it one way or the other, Mam said, not just a fondness for the drink, something more. They never could keep a job down, any of them, even when there was any work, and there wasn't any now anyway. Dad used to work on Gorton Parks. Used to leave his things out all ready for the morning down to the last detail, down to the one match wedged out of the matchbox all ready to strike his first cigarette of the day.

They didn't see so much of Uncle Edmund because Mam said Auntie Isabel was an old witch. Uncle Edmund and Auntie Isabel had nine children, Uncle John and Auntie Grace thirteen at the last count. Sutton Estate teemed with Holloways.

'Whenever you see Grace,' said Mam, 'she's got one at the breast and one in the belly,' and it was true. Auntie Grace sat by the fire, newly lit for the evening, suckling a small bald head, baby-white trails of shawl dangling milkily. 'Sit down, chuck,' she said, looking up. 'Your Uncle John'll get you some tea in a minute.'

There was always a welcome at Uncle John's. The table was set and Uncle John was counting heads. The kettle shrilled on the hob.

'And how's that grand lad?' Asked Uncle John. Auntie Grace's small snub face beamed. They were all mad for Bobby. Everyone was. When he was a tiny baby and Vi used to take him out on the front in his pram, everyone wanted him. Then his hair grew white-blond and the dimple in his chin deepened and his face was so impish and cheeky that it could make you laugh just to look at it, and everyone wanted to pick him up or ruffle his hair or sit him on their knees. And when being naughty got him an indulgent and slyly proud laugh as well as a telling off, and his waywardness garnered more admiration than censure in the grand scheme of things, Bobby decided to lark about as a way of life. Doing it got him adored, swaddled and coddled; and, always, allowances were made.

'Now then,' said Uncle John, picking up Auntie Grace, chair, baby, big round belly and all, lifting her to the newspaper-covered table. On every plate there was a thick slice of bread and marge and a banana. 'Now then,' he said, again, turning to take the kettle off the hob and pour the steaming stream of boiling water into an enormous stained brown teapot. 'Seen anything of your Auntie Benny, have you? Isabel said she was round our Edmund's last night.'

'No,' said Violet, 'I thought you might have.'

The mention of Bennet brought a quickening of excitement. Auntie Grace made a tutting sound and shook her head.

'Oh well,' said Uncle John, 'no doubt she'll make her appearance in due time. Here, Ruby, pass this to your mam. Berenice, get me a knife.'

He lined up the cups and jam jars, took down from the top of the cupboard a big roasting tin, the one he always made his sponge cake in.

'Benny only comes when she wants something,' Auntie Grace said, cutting her piece of bread and marge with her free hand.

'True enough.' Uncle John carved out slabs of cake, meticulous. He was like Dad, small and thin, exact in his movements.

'And what she wants,' Auntie Grace continued, 'like as not is a bed for the night. So she won't come here.'

'There you are, lamb.'

Violet sat with Ruby and Berenice and was given a proper cup, but Nell and Bob drank hot tea and condensed milk out of jam jars. Uncle John's sponge cake was always delicious, moist and warm and golden with a dark crust round the edges.

'Oh well,' said Uncle John, sitting in to the table, 'if you see her, tell her not to be such a stranger.'

'Well, she's got a bloody cheek if she thinks she's showing her face round here again after last time,' Mam said.

'Shut your bloody mouth, woman, you're so mean you wouldn't give a dying man the pickings of your nose.' Dad sat polishing his brasses.

'Ugh!' said Bobby, ceasing for a moment from popping his blown-up cheek with his finger, 'As if he'd want them.'

Nell and he, sitting together in one chair, giggled. Violet was getting ready to go round to her friend Josie Spedding's, standing in front of the fire looking into the mirror and tinkering with her rolls of hair. She pulled one of her daft long faces in the mirror at them, and they giggled the more.

'Dirty bugger!' said Mam, her round face punished and aggrieved.

'What did she do last time?' asked Nell.

'You mind your own business.' Her mouth went into a line.

'What did she do, Dad?'

'She didn't do anything.'

Mam could click her tongue so loudly to express disapproval it was like a big dog lapping. She walked heavily into the kitchen and the atmosphere plunged. Dad looked down at the brass dog he was rubbing with Dura-Glit and scowled, his hollowing face drawn and drooping. Bobby went back to popping his cheek and Violet pinched a little colour into her wan cheeks. Violet had a mannish face, like Dad's. It wasn't fair, Nell thought, that Violet resembled Dad more than she did. *She* wanted to look like Dad. She was nothing like him. But he was hers more than anyone else's because no one else could love him as much as she did. Wells of tenderness rose inside her at the sight of him, because he was the one she studied when she was very small, not Mam, who was always out cleaning. He was the one that was always there, because he was hardly ever in work; he was the one who got them dressed and fed them and bathed them in turns in the tin tub with his fag hanging out of his mouth. 'Dad!' They'd cry. 'Dad! Your smoke's going in my eye!' So she knew what was going on in his mind just as if she was in there with him, knew when he was happy or sad or worried or just trying to pluck up courage to ask Mam for an extra fourpence for a packet of Woodbines.

Right now he was thinking of his sister Bennet: Beautiful Benny Brown on the Hippodrome playbill, his childhood playmate, the charming young lady with the dazzling smile and cloud of dark hair on the lid of the chocolate box. She'd had her pictures taken for calendars. The music hall star Harold Whelan had proposed to her, the one who came on stage pulling on a pair of white kid gloves and whistling his signature tune. Mad for Auntie Bennet, he'd been, but she'd turned him down.

'You be back here by nine,' Mam snapped peevishly at Violet, stomping in from the kitchen.

'Oh Mam!' Violet's face fell. 'It's Saturday night. I'm only popping round to Josie's.'

'Don't you *Oh Mam* me. Nine o'clock.'

Violet sighed.

'*You* tell her, Sam.' Mam went back into the kitchen and started banging about in the pantry. You could hear her grumbling to herself.

'Dad!'

'You can't argue with your mam,' muttered Dad with a defeated shrug. If it had been either Bob or Nell he'd have stuck up for them and got in a row with Mam over it, but he wouldn't stick up for Violet.

'It's not fair,' said Violet quietly.

'Life's not,' he said, lighting his cigarette.

'Oh well.' She straightened her jumper. 'I don't mind coming back early if Auntie Benny's here.' She smiled. 'Are these two staying up?'

'Aw, go on, Dad, can we stay up for Auntie Bennet?'

'No you bloody well can't.' Mam was in the kitchen doorway. 'You can get to bed your normal time.'

'Oh God, I'm off,' said Vi.

'Violet!' Dad said sternly, 'You will not take the Lord's name in vain.'

The argument between Mam and Dad simmered on and off all night till Nell and Bob were in bed. Nell was reading *The Yellow Fairy Book*. She loved reading and she loved the fairy books by Andrew Laing. But it was hard to concentrate because Bobby was scratching like a demon on the other side of the big double bed they shared, and she was listening all the time to the different footsteps coming along their road, listening to see if any of them sounded like high heels, if any stopped at their gate. But they never did. Then she was scratching too.

'Shout down,' said Bobby.

'Dad!' She shouted, 'Dad!'

'I've got a flea!' Called Bob.

Up came Dad. Slowly, methodically, he began the trawl through their nighties, his old Union shirts that were thick and warm.

'Got you, you little bugger,' he said.

Pop! went the flea between his two thumbs.

Then he went through the bedclothes and sheets and pillows, frowning with concentration. Dad knew all about fleas and lice because of the war. You never saw anything like the fleas in the trenches, he said. And that was the least of it. The rats used to run about all over you, cheeky little buggers, not a bit scared, they'd eat the laces out of your boots while you were wearing them. Just run over you, he said, as if you were an old sack. You got used to it.

Mam stood in the doorway with her moaning face. 'They don't catch them here,' she said, 'it's that school. This house is spotless. Even if I do have to spend all the weekend on my hands and knees as well as slaving in other people's houses; and all the sheets and pillow slips are washed without fail once a week no matter what, so you can't blame me.'

'Nobody's blaming you,' Dad said.

'Dirty buggers they are round here, some of them.'

When she changed the sheets she dabbed their hair with paraffin. It worked pretty well and was safe enough so long as they didn't go anywhere near a naked flame for a bit.

'It's that dog,' she said.

'The dog never comes up here. Why don't you take that face off you, woman?'

'What face?'

'You know.'

'Well, it's alright for some, isn't it?' She exploded, going red, 'it's not as if she even lets on when she's arriving, she just turns up like Lady Muck and I don't know what she thinks, we're all just sitting there waiting for her to walk in? How'm I supposed to know whether or not to save a bit of dinner?'

'It's nowt to do with you.' Pop, another flea. 'I'll make stew. It can keep warm.'

Mam's eyes were hurt. 'Make me sick!' She spat and flounced off downstairs.

'Your Mam,' Dad muttered, 'she wouldn't just cast the first stone, she'd be there handing them out.'

They tittered and Dad chuckled, tucked them up and turned off the light, and for a long time they just lay there talking while Dad and Mam moaned away at each other familiarly downstairs.

'Tell me a ghost story,' Bob said.

'There was a big ball of red worms all wriggling about.'

She didn't know where she'd seen it but she knew she had.

'Yeah?'

'And it was in the corner of the room. Downstairs by the front door. Only it's invisible, and it rolls about like a big ball catching at people's legs and they don't know it's there. And sometimes it rolls about the house in the night and it rolls up the stairs and up onto the bed . . .'

'So what?' Said Bob. 'That's not ghosts. Tell a proper story.'

So she told him the one about Uncle Sidney on his way home late one night, how he met a man and asked him the time, and the man said: 'Time for the living to be in bed and time for the dead to walk,' and when Uncle Sidney looked down he saw that instead of feet the man had cloven hoofs.

Auntie Bennet didn't turn up. Vi came back about ten and Mam played hell. Nelly heard their voices nagging backwards and forwards, Mam shrill and Violet complaining; then she heard Vi go to bed, and Mam and Dad go to bed, and then it was quiet and everyone was asleep.

Bennet came on Sunday evening when the church bells were ringing, walking down their street with that proud head-in-the-air walk, sending echoes from the houses opposite with her dainty little heeled shoes clicking and clacking as her tiny feet side-stepped this way and that through the manure from the rag and bone man's horse.

Mam sighed. 'Violet, you can get in with the kids,' she said.

'Hiya, Benny.' Dad stood on the doorstep to welcome her. The kids crowded behind him.

'Hiya, Sam.' She put her hands up and kissed him. Her perfume wafted in, sweet and flowery, like the roses that grew in Granny and Grandad's garden in Morland. She came in and kissed everyone, and there was another smell from off her breath, sour and not very nice, like the smell on Dad's breath first thing in the morning when he'd come home drunk the night before. Nell always felt clumsy beside her little aunties. 'Do you know,' Bennet said, sitting down by the fire, 'it is *the* most glorious evening. Makes you wish you were out in the country.'

She'd been very beautiful, Auntie Bennet. You could still see it, something to do with the way she moved, delicately. And she spoke very sedately, never common or dropping her aitches like everybody else. They had a picture of Molly sitting on a chair with Bennet standing beside her with her hand on the back of the chair. They were both very young in the picture. Molly was actually the prettier of the two, with short, boyish hair, wide-set eyes and teeth that were very slightly buck but nicely so. Bennet had thin features and a faintly bird-like look. But Bennet was the one who knew what to do and went for the glamour in a big way, the hair, the make-up, the smile, the vivacity. She still had it, though there were lines now in the corners of her eyes and around her mouth, and the skin of her throat had a drawn, sinewy look. Nelly was never sure how she was supposed to feel about Auntie Bennet. Something had gone wrong with her and she didn't live like everybody else, but she was exciting; no one else she knew had an auntie who'd been on the stage and could sing and dance and juggle.

'Well well well, my chickadees!' She cried gaily, taking off her hat and fishing for a cigarette in her bag. 'How you doing, Violet, love?'

Violet was her favourite because Vi had been taken to Morland when she was a baby, after her mother died having her. Dad and his brothers were fighting in France in the big war, the terrible war. Vi had been Benny and Molly and Lal's baby doll. 'I'm smashing, Benny,' she beamed.

'Working?'

'Oh aye, same place.'

'How are *you*, Bessie?' Auntie Bennet asked Mam, flashing her a smile. 'Keeping well?'

'Can't complain.' Mam was civil if unsmiling. She went to put the kettle on. Bennet and Dad sat one on either side of the fireplace. Bennet put her lovely fine-boned feet up on the fender and waggled them about playfully in the dainty shoes, the kind she always wore to show them off.

'I saw our Lal in London,' she said, waving the still unlighted cigarette about. 'Little Victor's a picture. Oh, a charmer!'

London was worlds away. Lal lived in London with her husband and baby. London. Paris. Bennet got about. Dad hung on her words. Lal was doing fine. Looked well. Bennet threw back her cloud of black hair, still fluffy like it was on the picture they had, the one from the calendar, where she was showing her shoulders. She put the cigarette between her lips and seemed about to light it but withdrew it instead. 'Now,' she said teasingly, smiling around, 'I wonder what I've got in my bag.'

Three little pokes of pineapple rock, one for Nell, one for Bobby and one for Violet, 'Because I know you like it, Vi, even though you're not a child any more.' And a book for Violet too. With lots of pictures. *Tales from Shakespeare* by Charles and Mary Lamb. Then Bennet eased off her shoes and lit the cigarette, stretching her throat right back to blow smoke up to the ceiling. The way she smoked was like sucking candy and made you want to have some.

'Had your tea, Benny?' Dad said, leaning down to poke the fire.

They could hear Mam banging about in the kitchen. 'Violet!' She called sharply. Violet looked at the ceiling and went.

'I've had a bite, Sam,' said Auntie Bennet. She was so thin, like a bird, she looked as if she never ate. Drank like a fish though, Mam said. That was what had gone wrong with Auntie Bennet.

The drink, Mam said. That, and men. Nell didn't really know what that meant. Such a proud and pretty little creature, so bright, and yet she seemed so nervous too.

'Tell you what though, Sam.' Suck, suck. 'Couldn't let me bed down on the floor in here tonight, could you?'

Mam was leaning in the doorway, plump arms folded over her flowery pinny.

Dad didn't say anything straight away. He scratched his ear.

'Where've you been staying?'

'Here and there,' she said quickly. 'Just for tonight, Sam.' She smiled briefly but her eyes were scared. But then they weren't scared any more, they had never been scared, they were merry and defiant. 'Ah, go on Sam,' she said softly.

'And what about tomorrow night?' Sam asked, 'What about that one and the one after, Benny?'

She laughed. 'Consider the lilies of the field,' she said, 'take no thought for the morrow. Or something.' And she laughed again till tears came into her eyes.

'It's OK if our Benny stops, isn't it, Bessie?' Dad looked over his shoulder, but Mam just shrugged and went off to boss Violet in the kitchen.

'Sure,' he whispered gruffly. 'Sure you can stay.'

'One night, Sam. I've got a start in Liverpool. No kidding. Hey listen, Sam, what do you think of this for a coincidence? This is how I know it's genuine. My friend Polly Harkin, you won't credit where she's living. Erskine Street! Erskine Street! Oh Sam, do you remember? Well, I thought, Erskine Street, I can't turn that down. I ran into her on Deansgate and she gave me her address and I couldn't believe it! She was going back there. To Liverpool! Oh Sam! And she knows this fellow, you see, who has a very nice little club apparently, very pleasant, she says. Well, she says, you must come . . .'

She went on, prattling, gaining poise with every turn of her head.

'Are you going to stay the night, Auntie Bennet?' Asked Bob.

Violet was bringing in the big wooden tray with the tea things. Mam followed, blank-faced, carrying the sugar bowl.

'You'd better ask your mam,' Auntie Bennet said, smiling.

Mam plonked the sugar down. 'Our Violet can go in with these two,' she said.

'That's it, you're a sport, Bessie.' Bennet, grinning all over her face, took the cup and saucer Vi fondly handed her. Her thin hands were shaky and there was a slop.

'Well, that's that then,' said Dad, pouring the sweet red tea into his saucer.

Late that night, when everyone else was in bed, Sam and Bennet sat up, talking and smoking cigarettes. While Bobby slept with his hands thrown back above his head on the pillow as if he were being held up at gunpoint, Nell and Vi conversed in whispers so as not to disturb Mam next door. She was terrible for coming in if you talked, standing there in the light from the door in her long white flannel nightie with her stomach sticking out and her hairnet on. 'Shut your bloody mouths,' she'd say, 'Have you seen the time? Christ!' Don't say that, Dad would scold if he were there. Our Lord is not a swear word!

Later maybe Bennet produced a bottle from somewhere, because she started singing. She sang *Just Like The Ivy*, and Vi and Nell were quiet, holding their breath, till they heard her stop and laugh softly before starting on *Two Little Girls in Blue*. Stifling laughter, they crept out onto the landing, tip-toed halfway down the stairs and sat side by side to listen. Dad sang *McCafferty* in his stern voice, as he always did, and then they both sang together: *Lily of Laguna*, and *Sonny Boy*, and *Little Pal*, *If Daddy Goes Away*, which was Vi's favourite and always made her cry. Then came the spirituals, beginning with *Poor Old Joe*, Nell's favourite:

Gone are the days when my heart was young and gay . . .

Sitting half asleep on the stairs, the sound was heartbreaking, floating in the dark. Dad's was his usual bass growl but Bennet had a lovely voice. Clear as a bell. Bennet didn't just sing the words like everybody else, she made you feel them, like little sharp knives pricking you into tears, so that when she softly called: *I'm coming! I'm coming!* A wondrous wistful rising lilt, you saw cottonfields and a high sun, and a chariot swinging down from pink and gold clouds like a swingboat at the fair; and you were poor black Joe whose head bent low, yearning for the golden shore.

Dad and Benny were closest together in age of all their brothers and sisters. Their voices together were like a twined thread, used to one another. They sang:

Way down upon the Swannee River far, far away

They sang of golden days gone by, gone for ever, yearning never satisfied, never filled, and all the closest bed-warm days of brother and sister, and sister and sister, and anyone and anyone wrapped up warm together –

Gone.

Nelly drooped against Vi, who sang under her breath, while a tear tracked slowly down her cheek:

All up and down the whole creation
Sadly I roam
Still looking for the old plantation
And for the old folks at home.

Dad told them how they used to sell the poor slaves away from their families: the idea of someone taking you and selling you away from everyone you knew. Away from Mam and Dad and Bobby and Violet and everyone.

All the world is sad and dreary, everywhere I roam . . .

Their voices soared.

Then Dad recited his favourite poem, the one he did sometimes after he'd got back from the pub. In her mind's eye, Nelly on the stairs saw him linking his fingers over his chest as he lay back in his chair, eyes glazing over as he gazed at the ceiling:

Sunset and evening star
And one clear call for me . . .

Bennet didn't get up till after ten, long after Mam, who cleaned from nine till four for half a crown, had gone off to work. She didn't eat any breakfast, just sat in front of the fire and smoked a few cigarettes while Dad cleaned up. She was off for the Liverpool train, she said; then she kissed the children and put on her coat, and Dad shoved a couple of bob in her pocket as he kissed her goodbye on the doorstep. She seemed sad. Then she was gone.

Nelly remembered she hadn't told her about not being such a stranger to Uncle John. Too late. Anyway, maybe she didn't go there so much because she couldn't afford to buy all those packets of pineapple rock.

There was a row when Mam came home. There always was after Auntie Bennet's visits. Mam found Bennet's dirty tea cup from this morning still down by the side of her chair next to the fireplace. She'd been working all bloody day she said and she wasn't coming home to a pigsty. She wasn't used to those kind of filthy conditions even if some others were who could rot in bed all day while decent people got up and went out scrubbing bloody floors on their hands and knees to put food on the table.

Dad was dishing up sausage and mash, dollop, dollop, dollop. Dad did all the cooking.

'Shut your bloody mouth,' he said. 'Can't even get through the door without your bloody moaning.'

'I've got a right to!'

Two sausages apiece, but Dad always pretended he didn't want his and popped one on Nelly's plate and one on Bob's. Poor old Violet, of course, didn't qualify for an extra one because she was near enough an adult, or at least not a proper child any more.

Mam and Dad went on at each other all through tea and right on into the evening. The kids went and played out on the front, like they always did. They were on Dad's side. No matter what, all of them were always on Dad's side whenever there was a fight, and there were always fights. It was still going on when they went back in. Mam had found out about the couple of bob he'd given Bennet and was screaming that she didn't go out slaving all day to put money in Benny's pockets, let her put money in her own pockets, she can do, you know what she is, we all do, she'll not go short. Then he slapped her across the face and she kicked him and punched him in the chest, and they set to for a while till Mam broke a plate on his head and made it bleed.

'Dad's bleeding,' Bobby said.

'Serves him bloody right!' said Mam. 'Violet! Go and get your dad a plaster.'

Joolz Denby
Trouble

Inspired by Iceberg Slim's novel Pimp *– this story has been drawn from real life; names have been changed to protect the innocent.*

I live in Bradford. It's a stone built city in the North of England, crouched in a wide valley like a refugee finding safe haven. Above us, as we plod round town or stumble down the Leeds road, the skies unfurl like tattered banners; blue, concealing, cloud embroidered. Once it was a wealthy place, very wealthy; great families made fortunes from woollen cloth. They built monuments to their beloved money; rearing sandstone palaces crusted over with decorative carving as thick as the family Bibles that recorded their lives. In Gothic niches, blind craggy saints and kings stare into the grey; adamantine queens and petrified sailing ships stud fretted façades; ropes and swags of deathless ivy and acanthus drape and festoon in perpetual glory; the stone rendered almost liquid by the mason's skill.

The money's gone now. It's been gone a long time and now the city rags along in an unravelling tatter of poverty. We live here; we eat sag alloo and Peshwari naan, and drink thick, yellow mango lassi at midnight in basement curry houses. If we need fresh air, we go to the moors and clamber round the gritstone crags that punch up from the earth like fists and mirror in nature those buildings we walk past every day. The city still hides itself, a strange place no stranger knows, cloaked in a scruffy pall of 1960s town planning. It's a crazy stone puzzle, an empty castle, decayed and abandoned, inhabited now only by squabbling tribes who build camp fires in the big hall at night, to keep off devils and the terrible stars.

Just out of the town centre are the tall, slab-fronted mills, long abandoned by the clattering looms or whirling spindles. A couple of these have been colonized by musicians looking for a place to make noise all night without the neighbours ringing the coppers. We've got a studio in one of these hives – a room facing out on the long road heading to the country; but there's nothing rural here. It's where the prostitutes work, since the vigilantes drove them out of Manningham. It's a dark canyon of six-storey ex-industrial nowhere, it's got a hundred nooks and ginnels, alleys and dead ends, and in winter, it's witchy cold and the rain drives in sideways sheets as the wind tumbles a scurfy scum of rubbish along the pavements and slaps old plastic bags and crisp packets round the girl's skinny ankles.

Up and down, they walk, all night long. At three in the morning when, they say, the dying give up the ghost, they suck off punters in parked cars or shuffle from foot to foot, waiting and hoping, their pinched faces pushing out of the dark, pallid as blisters. The cars slow down, the newer girls hastily stitch an imitation of a smile onto their icy faces because the punters like it if you smile and say *'looking for business, love'* in a bright way; it makes them feel the whole deal is a bit personal, a bit tart-with-a-heart-of-gold. The more experienced girls can't be bothered with all the fake chumminess, it's too much effort, and it's much easier to fuck someone you loathe than smile at them. Not that the punters know that, not really. I don't know what the punters actually think, if they think at all – but if they think the girls like them, or like sex, or like their lives, God help them, because it's a fool with his foot on the road to Hell who lives in blind ignorance of *that* kind of truth.

If a punter wants something more adventurous than can be done easily in a vehicle, they'll take him to a bit of waste ground across the road from our building. Amongst the woody thickets of buddleia and Japanese knotweed, there's a bit of plastic sheeting thrown over a couple of pallets, garnished with an old sofa cushion bursting it's filthy raggled guts from weather and damp. There the girls do what they do; in the mouldy stink, in the rain, in the bone scraping frost, for a tenner or maybe even for twenty, if they don't use a condom. Then when the punter shuffles off they jack up, smoke, or if they're very new, cry.

The girls have learnt that our building is used by musicians, and stopped bothering with the patter when the lads pull up in their beaten-up wreckers. If anything, they've got used to seeing us loading and unloading music gear at odd hours and getting on the tour bus, or working through until dawn. Now they wave, sometimes, or beg for fags, or lifts up to the gas station, or tell the lads if they've left the car lights on, or tap them for a few pence if it's a slow night. It's a kind of truce – not friendship, not like we're mates or anything. It's just that we're not straight, not from the straight world; we're not in the Life, but we're not social workers, or citizens, do-gooders, reporters or punters. So we balance on the blade's edge – uneasy allies in an invisible war. It's a delicate kind of peace, though, always just a breath away from trouble.

And trouble always comes, whether you like it or not.

Our building isn't finished, the conversion to studios and rehearsal rooms costs money and the weasely hippy who masterminds this warren constantly runs out of cash. Sometimes he has all night bongo parties or gigs in the ground floor. This, plus the fact he's daubed the rotting brick with Day-Glo murals has led to the belief in that wannabe London – Leeds – that Bradford is covertly harbouring a genuine, authentic underground music scene. Well, that's as maybe, as they say round here. So anyhow, after the *über*-hippy has a rent party, he does some building work. This is carried out mainly by Steve.

You'd never notice Steve in a crowd. You'd never give him a second glance. He's a short, silent, thin bloke in his late forties; an ex-drop-out from the 1970s. He wears ancient Lennon specs with bottle-bottom lenses so greasy and fingerprinted I'm surprised he can see out of them, knackered old work clothes and his straggle of mousy hair is slipping slowly backwards. He's a no-colour person, if you know what I mean – sometimes, if the light's right, he almost seems transparent. But he's an excellent carpenter, and he lives in that enclave of pot-heads who so successfully drove the junkies out of their street and now exist in a kind of semi-legal herb heaven. Steve has seen a bit of life; he's had his share of knocks, he likes to say when you can coax a word out of him, but now he's got a family, kids; he's OK – and behind the opaque lenses, his sky-blue Northern eyes flicker with love.

Trouble

Oh, one thing I may not have mentioned, is that the prostitutes round by the studio are children. Not one of them is over sixteen and some of them are twelve or thirteen. They are not the feisty, seasoned pros of legend who may, or may not, exist outside the popular press and TV dramas. These girls are just that – girls. Most are drug addicts or alchies, or both. They're ruined by the savagery of their brief infancies and they're riddled with diseases ranging from chlamydia and clap, through to multiple drug resistant syphilis and AIDS. Some of them have PID, some TB. Some of them know they're dying. Cold sores tattoo their rosy, unformed mouths and their eyes are black jelly. They wear tight, imitation club wear market stall fashions and never wash their make-up off, just add more layers until it forms a cacky mask. They shake a lot and their minds are shot by what they've known and smelt and seen and done, so straight folk often think they're thick.

The girl I'll call Marie was in better shape than some. She was mixed race; her freckles stood out like paint splatter under the harsh sodium street light. She always wore her fluffy, tea-coloured hair scraped back with gel into a pony tail that exploded into curls and was pulled so tight it lifted the corners of her long, storm-grey eyes. She usually wore a silver puffa jacket, so she stuck out a bit from the others. But she looked as if she ate, she didn't chain smoke but chewed gum instead, and her gaze was still fairly level and engaged. There was some life left in her face. One night, as we drove away from the studio, we saw her playing hopscotch to pass the time; one, two, one, two, turn on one leg. She was concentrating, her tongue stuck out a little, her forehead creased. Tall for her age, a gawky thirteen year old all knees and bony wrists; leggy, like an unbroken colt.

Watching her drove Steve mad. He couldn't bear it. She reminded him, he said, of his eldest daughter. He couldn't stand to think of what that little lass did at night – what all those little lasses did – when his girl was tucked up safe in bed at home. It wasn't right. It wasn't fair. What was wrong with a world that could let this happen? He could only talk in clichés, not being a speaking type of man, but his words were strong because they were true and truth, Steve thought, would prevail, as would justice. His anger burnt slow and steady, brooding banked under his good hippy hatred of violence and conflict and all that chunter about sex workers and prostitute's unions the women's groups his partner belonged to favoured. His fury made me feel guilty, more than guilty, ashamed. The anger I'd felt when we first set up in the building and I'd seen the age of the girls and their life, had been eaten away by the everydayness of the whole thing. I'd got used to seeing the girls. I'd got used to making my excuses about there being nothing I could do, to not thinking about it. His anger was fresh, it was re-born every dawn, it was wick and pure. It turned and coiled and twisted in him like a fiery serpent biting it's own tail. It wouldn't go away.

Then, one night he was helping clear up after a gig downstairs, and as he took the rubbish out of the side door, he saw Marie's pimp's car pull up. Not a posh stretch limo. Not a sleek ebony Lexus or a silver BMW with a personal plate saying *Mack 1*. Just a ratty blue Cavalier with a bead cover on the driver's scat and a *Magic Tree* hanging from the rearview. And the pimp was no slouch hatted, mink coated, lover-lover man, diamonds in his gold teeth and one long fingernail to snort off. Marie's pimp looked like any big, heavy set, beer-bellied, out of shape bloke you'd see round town in TK Maxx or Burger King. He was bleary-eyed, stubble-chinned and wearing a footie shirt, shell trousers with Adidas up the side and a heavy gold Figaro chain. But Steve knew him, knew what he was. He'd seen him drop Marie off and pick her up, even seen her hand over the takings one night. And he lost it, he lost it *big* style.

Dropping the bulging black plastic bag, he strode towards the pimp, every inch of his slight body rigid with righteous ire. One of the lads who had been helping him clear up said that at that point, everything went into slow motion; the air turned to treacle. They started towards Steve, convinced he was going to get the living shit kicked out of him, but they weren't quick enough to grab him.

He stood in front of the big man, his head on a level with that winking gold chain, his bony, callused finger prodding the guy's breastbone.

'You, you f-fuckin' bastard – you should f-fuckin' be ashamed of yersel – a little lass like that; I know what you are, you – you . . . I'm gonna . . .'

The pimp pulled back, a surprised look on his jowly face, then as he started to respond, a sliver blur launched itself from out of the shadows and Steve was shoved hard sideways, his glasses flying into the gutter.

'*Get off my dad! You – get off my dad . . .*'

Marie's shrill voice echoed through the narrow side street like a piece of shiny cloth tearing. Her father grabbed her by her pony tail and yanked her off Steve, spinning her round and shoving her into the road. Steve swayed, his face drained of blood, his myopic eyes blinking.

'That's yer – that's yer daughter? Fer fuck's sake – *yer pimpin' yer own daughter?*'

The big fella sneered, then laughed harshly. 'Huh, yeah – an' what the fuck is it ter do wi' you, yer little fucker? It's my fuckin' kid, I can do what I like wi' her – it's none o' yer fuckin' business, right?'

Steve fell back, away from Marie's father, unable to think of any reply, unable to think at all. The big man copped a glance at the lads who were now tumbling through the door, tripping over rubbish bags and shouting Steve's name. Smacking a lone, four-eyed little nutter was one thing, dealing with four or five lads was another. He redirected his irritation at Marie, shouting at her for causing him hassle and ordering her to get in the car. She folded herself into the passenger seat, her lower lip stuck out like a five year old, and you didn't have to be a psychic to know she was saying it wasn't her fault, it wasn't, she didn't even know that bloke, honest.

They drove off.

The lads reached Steve as he was fumbling around for his specs. They comforted him as best they could, they got him a cuppa with loads of sugar and they sat with him while he drank it and wiped his eyes, long tremors shaking his legs as the adrenaline left his system. None of them knew what to say; nothing would make it all all right or make any real sense of the whole congealed mess.

Marie didn't come back to the road by our building, but none of us fooled ourselves she'd found salvation. There are plenty of other streets, and brothels, and saunas and portacabins on industrial deadlands where girls do fifty punters on a Saturday and have to piss in a bucket. Steve never talks about what happened, what he tried to do; he has turned back into himself and is quieter than ever, the brief blinding fire in his heart gone to ashes and cold cinders.

But I thought about it for a long time; and this is what I thought.

Love is both marvellous and terrible, we all know that; at least we do if we've lived past thirty. When it's marvellous – full of wonders and miracles – it's as blindingly beautiful as a great angel clothed in the gold of the undying sun; it's as breathtaking as nature and as small and powerful as a child's hand in yours. Love like this fills every cell of your body, it's honey-sweet, pure and without taint; it redeems and demands no return. It's truth and justice; it's hope and joy and it smiles like your beloved on a clean Spring morning; it's gentle, tender and not of the World.

And love is terrible; nothing is so terrible as bad love. It's not romantic or daring or glamorous, there's nothing good in it, nothing nourishing. When I think of it, I see the image of a card from an old French tarot pack I used to use when I was in the fortune-telling game. It's from the major arcana – the 'picture cards' my punters used to call them. The card is called '*Le Diable*', – The Devil. It's one of the worst cards to get, really; I used to wince if anyone turned it up. On it, drawn in a crude woodcut style, is the Devil, standing on a little box or platform. He's not beautiful Lucifer, Son of the Morning, or some suave Satan in designer threads; he's sloppy fat, a brute, sweaty creature with a fuckwit smirk and leathery, vestigial wings. He's wearing nothing but some baggy leggings. His belly and tits push out bloated and coarse. In each of his blubbery hands is a leash, and attached to the leashes are a man, and a woman. They're naked and on their mewling faces are expressions of horrible, unclean pleasure; they are gazing, twisted up and back, at the Devil, with deathless and immeasurable love in their brutalized eyes. They would do anything for their beloved master, and he knows it.

The meaning of the card is destruction, bondage, malevolence; it's violence, fatality, self-punishment and black magic. It's horror and it's the abyss; it's every foul thing, every humiliation, every scourge and every filthy degradation a human being can live through, and some they can't. Only when the card presents reversed, is there hope, and then it's a long hard road back to the light.

Steve saw the Devil card that night, in Marie's father, in the vast, inherited ignorance of that man's daily, unthinking cruelty. He saw Marie, bound by bad love, by a terrible fate, to a father who used his child's passionate desire to love and be loved as a means to get money so he could buy himself beer, cigarettes and cheap gold jewellery.

And every little prostitute on that dark road does it for love; for the promise of love, for the flimsy and idiot illusion of love peddled to them by pimps and users; they suffer and they die, they are illuminated and they sacrifice everything, for the hope, *just the hope*, of love.

Oh, oh, beautiful and terrible; and everything for love.

image: howard devoto (on the right) & pete shelley

As a founder-member of Manchester's *Buzzcocks*, Howard Devoto featured as lyricist and vocalist on 1977's seminal *Spiral Scratch* ep. He later formed *Magazine*, pursued a solo career and worked with the guitarist Noko in *Luxuria* before leaving the music business in 1990. A recent collaboration with fellow Buzzcock Peter Shelley (as *ShelleyDevoto*) produced the album *Buzzkunst* (Cooking Vinyl, 2002) whose lyrics are printed here.

Howard Devoto
Lyrics & Poetry

A World To Give Away

I'm dashing through paradise
I'm so polite in what I say
I'm lost in the age I'm in
so I want a world to give away

I know what's mine
you'll learn what's yours
I know what you want to see
you scratch my back and I grow claws
we're failing in love awkwardly

Now we're dashing through paradise
we're so polite in what we say
lost in the age we're in
we only want a world to give away

A world to give away
we only want a world to give away

Now I'm dancing in my own good time
with my words sticking out of your face
if you're not feeling weak today I know
someone who will take your place

I know what's mine
you'll learn what's yours
I know what you want to see
you scratch my back and I grow claws
we're failing in love awkwardly

Now I'm dancing in my own good time
with my words sticking out of your face
if you're not feeling weak today
I know that somebody will take your place

I only want a world to give away
I only want a world to give away

– 1978, 2001

SELF-DESTRUCTION

We're talking self-destruction . . .

You didn't ask to be born
you never ever asked to be born
well, don't look at me
we didn't ask for you to be born either
so take along a little make-up
for all of your mistakes
then take a bow
a last look round
pull the lever

Self-destruction – we're enthralled
self-destruction – cos you've been called
self-destruction – a minor skirmish
self-destruction – I wonder when my turn is?

Just do it . . .

I can't hear you screaming
so I guess I'll be OK
there's a lot to worry
when you're in the money
oh my manicure
oh my pedicure
my peace of mind
my vomit
ours is the land of the milk and the honey
we'd better bomb it

Self-destruction
self-destruction

It's fantastic!

Self-destruction – so, yes or no?
self-destruction – c'mon now, give it a go
self-destruction – it's yours to keep
self-destruction – c'mon on now, ya deep creep

Self-destruction – c'mon now, ya deep creep
self-destruction

It's a great idea!

Self-destruction – and we're enthralled
it's a minor skirmish
self-destruction – cos you've been called
boy, I wonder when my turn is?

– 2001

'TIL THE STARS IN HIS EYES ARE DEAD

He wants to cry until the stars in his eyes are really dead
he wants to cry until the stars in his eyes are really dead

He is poised to a very strange degree
wrapped up in emotional imagery
small and senseless, on an alter ego trip
he wants to alter your every ego trip

'Nothing personal
nothing to see me
nothing doing
nothing with me
nothing much
and nothing to do with me'

He wants to cry until the stars in his eyes are really dead
he wants to cry until the stars in his eyes are really dead

He is awash in competing theories
he's glad to be out of the house
it's that time of the evening
'I need to have some feelings'

'I'm all surface tension
present tension
keeps you going
gets you nowhere
no pretension
worst person singular'

He wants to cry until the stars in his eyes are really dead
he wants to cry 'til the stars in his eyes are really dead

Because the message is cheap and exhilarating
now he's slobbering on the glass
a sexistic boy, having a world wide wank
he says 'well, that's very punk of me'

'Nothing personal
nothing to see me
nothing doing
nothing with me
nothing much
and nothing to do with me'

He wants to cry until the stars in his eyes are really dead
he wants to cry 'til the stars in his eyes are dead

– 2001

CAN YOU SEE ME SHINING?

I'm pulling a face
the most gorgeous face
I'm in trouble with myself
I'm gonna save my precious skin
I'm gonna save my precious skin
by getting under your skin
can you see me shining?

Can you see me shining?
say you can see me shining
can you see me shining?
say you can see me shining

Is that some kind of trouble across the room?

Think I'm pulling a bird
I've been bothering-up myself
I'm dragging my nerves over your nerves
cos I've got to save my miserable skin
I've got to save my miserable skin
by getting under your skin
can you see me shining?

Shine for me . . .

Can you see me shining?
say you can see me shining
can you see me shining?
say you can see me shining

Some sunny day you'll see me shine.

Can you see me shining?
I'm shining out like I'm towering up in the night
shining out brightly from a blackening hole

Can you see me shining?
I'm shining out like I'm some big mutha of a searchlight
reaching right down to the bottom of your soul

We're arriving at the bottom of your soul.

My seed eats into me
cos I'm seedy
I am a dish
and it eats into me with relish
can you see me shining?
can you see me shining?

— 2001

GOING OFF

A sense of my finger on the pulse
the blue of the sky in my face
a name for the meaning I explode

A name for the meaning I call up
when my nerves are ringing back
I don't answer
I'm going off
I'm going off
off

We are the future, we're going off
we are the future, we're going off
there is a name for the meaning and threat
we're just about as far from death as you get

A sense of my finger on the pulse
the blue of the sky in my face
a name for the meaning I explode

A name for the meaning and the smell
the intimacy of your quantum state
your physical description
going off
going off
off

There is a name for the meaning I am
I'm making all the difference I can
I'm suffering against you
I'm suffering against you

We're going off
you know, we're not really nature
we're going off
we're not really nature
we're going off
we're not really nature
we're going off

— 2001

DEEPER

Our love
it might mean something
our love
unless it happens you know that we'll never ever know

My love
we're deeper than life
my love
you and I are deeper than these very simple times

Our love
the only show in town
our love
always deeper, going deeper, deeper than these times

We're going deeper
we're going deeper

Our love
it's a childish game
our love
turn around –
the cooling breeze
is now a hurricane

— 2001

STUPID KUNST

I did it
I made it
it's mine
in the fullness and the meanness of time

And now it's done
this is the one
and I am the one
the original one

It's by me, beside me
it's by me, beside me

All my own work
all my own work
it's all my own work
all my own work

You can admire
you know how to admire
I know I've seen your licence for hire

Seize the surface and repeat
seize the surface and repeat

– 2001

SYSTEM BLUES

Here's to blues in your nebulous face
divine like inspiration
familiar blues in your mouth
like something got flogged in creation
sex blues
blood blues
system blues
system blues
system blues

'Tell them its been wonderful' blues
I've been out and I've bought me the blues
I am a fucking stupid man blues
whole caboodle
dead hard blues
sex blues
blood blues
system blues
system blues
system blues

I can feel the weight
of the next world at my shoulder
strangeness blues on an afternoon
growing colder
sex blues
blood blues
system blues
system blues
system blues

– 2001

SO THERE I WAS

I was painted-up
I was disappointing
I was stirring
I was having it done

I was troubling
I was blindly calculating
how I was going on

So there I was, unintentionally funny . . .

It was a happy endings sort of thing, wasn't it?
Yes, and what's the point of that?

I was confidential
I was unreasoning
feeling so bad
I was fate
I was so sad
about how I was ending

So there I was, unintentionally funny . . .

(mutters) Fuck that,
(laughter)
Oh, I didn't mean . . .
(sighs)

Then I was thrown into this sort of zen apoplexy . . .

Why?

There I was, in deep
forever yours
finally asleep
stuck between your wars

There I was, a one face crowd
there I was, a stifled yawn
there I was, upon the fly
at either end of a thunder storm

So there I was
when the stars went up
the First Time
the First Time

So there I was, interrupted forever . . .

– 2001

Lynn Kramer
On Reading Apollinaire

YOU CAN FOLLOW THE RULES

OR   ADVENTURE

YOU   AN

CAN   HAVE

Some time ago I took a sea voyage for my health. Steamer rugs on deck and steaming mugs of bouillon while you contemplate the sea and sky that go on for ever. The emptiness could send you into a hospital with clean white beds and electric wires attached to your head.

I am invited to the Captain's cocktail party but I haven't got a frock. Frocks are de rigueur for these occasions. They are novel to me. I would like a black frock, well cut, close fitting but not too tight. A slit up the back in case I had to run for it. Black shoes with high heels I would kick off if it came to that. The notion of doing a runner on board the SS *Troubadour* – where would one run to? You can picture the scene: me on the top deck backed up against the rails in a force ten. Then what? My swimming is not up to these fantasies.

So, do I improvise with the cabin furnishings and go anyway? Drape myself in the oyster and tangerine silk-polyester counterpane, with the tiger skin pedestal rug from the en suite bathroom tucked round my shoulders against the evening chill.

On Reading Apollinaire

Stick a gold cigarette holder between my ruby lips. Nick the four inch stilettos waiting for a spit and polish outside door 339. Take those pampered cruisers by storm.

They'll cheer as I make my entrance. Amateur photographers will be out in force, cameras clicking, camcorders rolling. I'll be all over the ship's newspaper in no time. There's fame for you. It might even get into one of those snappy journals back home like *Hello!* magazine. It could change my life.

The alternative is not to go. Lie on my bunk and stare out of the porthole at a colourless ocean. Well, that's enough to get me up off my arse. What was that? The shoes might not fit? Where's your sense of adventure? I'll stuff cotton wool in the toes, cut down a pair of socks, I'll come up with something. And if they're too small I'll get a blister or two. You have to pay for your art, a performance doesn't happen without blood and bruises. I consider myself lucky I've been given the opportunity.

Unlike the poor sod sitting on the pavement outside Holland Park station with a dog. Sod as in sodden. Hoping to palm off last week's *Big Issue* on unsuspecting soft-hearted finance directors of over-valued companies that are about to be knocked off the FTSE 100. Where is his invitation? Is he going to spend the night here, a bit of polythene under his bum, a greasy rug, the dog whining?

What if I la di da'd up to him and offered him a bed for the night? What if he accepted? Would anyone in their right mind offer to take in a tramp? Or, if you prefer, a vagrant, mendicant, dosser, beggar, homeless person . . . a free spirit, rough sleeper, refugee, exile, deportee, outcast, displaced person . . . Not to mention the dog.

But if I –
and he said –

No, a relationship between two strangers is not like the weather. You can't forecast the tentative sunshine, a spring shower, the sudden sharp frost at night. And even meteorology is not an exact science, only the study of the processes and phenomena of the atmosphere.

Perhaps he would end up with my ivory-backed hairbrush in his grime-encrusted hand while I, spine erect and hardly daring to breathe, would perch on a Victorian piano stool upholstered in green velvet, my eyes fixed on the slender naked branches outside the window that were abandoned to the wind. He would draw the bristles through my tangled red bush. He would pull the brush down to the ends of my waist-length hair, each stroke a satisfaction and a provocation. And he would go on brushing until he could see his face in my glow.

And then –

And then reality would muscle in, as it always does. The hair brush would be clogged with a fuzz of hair and dust. The sod would still have a stink about him of stale beer and piss and dog, despite luxuriating in a bath perfumed with attar of roses and wild hibiscus. The telephone would ring, and a voice that might be male or female would inform me that my order for two dozen sea urchins was now ready for collection. And I would turn and look at him, this prince of the streets, and see an old man with holes where his eyes once were. Thrown out on the street my lover would wander back to Holland Park, only to find that a squatter had taken up residence on his greasy rug and he was homeless again.

And if it weren't a man it might be a shoe. You often see one abandoned in the gutter. One solitary shoe lying on its side. The cruelty of separating a couple who have never spent a night apart is heart-rending. And they don't just cast them off like a useless fancy, no, they have to kick 'em sideways like the *tok-tokkies* we used to flip onto their backs as children, immobilize them like a wheelchair user tipped out of their chair. Take me home, they cry, but nobody hears. The temptation to pick up that battered creature and cradle it, whisper reassurance and give it refuge, is immense. Shoes give their lives for us to walk all over them. We wear them out with our incessant demands. Donkeys are looked after with more respect.

This is history. But questions will be asked. The past must be made accountable.

Once upon a time that shoe was beautiful. Black patent leather, slender heel, long pointed toe, the instep bare. It reclined alongside its mirror image on a crimson couch in a window under a chandelier with a thousand lights. And sun-starved shoppers stopped and peered through and misted up the glass with their desire. A punk couple with their arms entwined, their studded tongues in each other's mouths. And then one day the shoes were gone, replaced by a couple of loafers, basket-weave, tan. The punks drifted off without even holding hands.

And the fading *coloratura*, still waiting for her time to come, giggled as she stepped into them. Declared, as she paraded around the unheated attic in front of her youthful lover who was impatient for her to come to bed, that she would never part with them. *Lentamente* she removed her clothes, dropping the garments one by one onto the old paint-spattered floorboards while he watched, his eyes sharpening green in the light from the slit in the faded curtain. Then, suppressing a shiver, she squeezed into bed beside him with her shoes on.

No, I'm not one for picking up rubbish in the street. If you sat down one sunny morning on the corner of your road you'd be rubbish by the evening. Even the refuse collectors wouldn't give you the time of day, they'd just heave you into their big trucks with all the other waste put out for recycling.

Opportunity is what it's about. Opportunity, opportunist. An opportunist is one who takes advantage of good fortune without regard for principles. Does the weather have principles? Is it fair in its parceling out of foggy mornings, breathtaking sunsets, drought, snow? What are principles? What is opportunity?

Here the sky is on the move. Nacreous clouds, the light breaking through, metamorphosis. There's nothing I can do about it. The spines of trees are silent now beyond the window. Then rain slants down past the sun, a naive blue sky pushes in, a bird flies straight through the middle, the shower is over. The sun strengthens, whitens the window ledges of the houses opposite, lifts the stern brick into festive mood. The clouds accelerate from right to left, the blue deepening, widening. A plane paints a white streak.

Excitement wears off like soles wear out and even mouth to mouth resuscitation won't revive it. Eventually it's time for the charity shop and the black plastic bag and space for the heart to expand. From the *coloratura*'s point of view the shoes are finished, they are part of a story that was once upon a time. She turns her back on them and when no one is looking tosses them out of the window. They fall together like a pair of dead swallows, graceful in their downward flight, until the wind hurls one off-course and flings it into a supermarket trolley wheeled by a man with matted hair and a grey overcoat belted with string. Who picks it up, croons *bellissima*, polishes it on the lapel of his coat and gives a toothless smile, which so frightens a little girl with plaits and a blue hat on her way to school that she fails her spelling test. And when she is grown up she writes a story about a toothless man in a dirty coat who smiled at her in the street one day and changed her life. And the other shoe falls straight down into the gutter where it knows it belongs.

On board ship there is no gutter. There is just First Class and Cabin Class. The Captain must host two cocktail parties, one for widows in fur stoles and too much gold around their scrawny necks. The other for the rest of us. A smoke-filled room, the roar of voices, a black man pounding a white piano: *I can't get enough of you.* Smile, darling, in your pedestal tiger skin, what's the worst that could happen?

Up on deck stars prick the blackness above my head. I stand at the rail and listen to the rhythms of the sea that will not be stilled. A man emerges from the shadows behind the lifeboats. It is too dark to see his face but I recognize the voice, the doggy smell. We reach into each other, he is naked beneath his coat, I bite his tender lip. We sink down onto the damp deserted deck till morning sweeps over us.

Biographical Notes

Howard Devoto see page 116.

Annie Murray's stories have been published in various magazines including *She* and *London Magazine*, and in the anthologies *Mouth* and *Her Majesty* (Tindal Street Press). Her seventh novel *Chocolate Girls* is shortly to be published by Macmillan.

Alan Jenkins' collections include *Harm* (Chatto & Windus), winner of the 1994 Forward prize for Best Collection; *The Drift* (Chatto & Windus) a Poetry Book Society Choice and nominated for the T. S. Eliot; *A Short History of Snakes* (Selected, Grove Press, USA); and *The Little Black Book* (Cargo Press). He is Deputy Editor of the *TLS*.

John Murray's most recent novel was *John Dory* (Flambard). His sixth novel *Jazz* (Flambard) will be published in 2003. In 1988 he won the Dylan Thomas Award for his stories. He was the editor of *Panurge*.

Charlie Boxer is the author of a novella, *The Cloud of Dust* (Cape).

David Hart's two books of poetry are *Setting the Poem to Words* and *Crag Inspector*. He has also won the National Poetry Competition, and been poet-in-residence at Worcester Cathedral, South Birmingham Mental Health, and the Aldeburgh Poetry Festival. He was Birmingham's Poet Laureate in 1997–1998.

Bernardine Evaristo is the award-winning author of two novels-in-verse *Lara* and *The Emperor's Babe*. Hamish Hamilton will publish, in 2003, her forthcoming novel *Soul Tourists*, from which 'The Burial Ground' is an extract. She is currently a Writing Fellow at Columbia University, New York.

Biographical Notes

Paul Magrath is a free-lance writer and editor whose work has appeared in a variety of publications including *The Independent*, *The Times*, *TLS*, *Literary Review*, *The Tablet* and *Areté*.

Jason Cowley is literary editor of the *New Statesman*. He writes for *The Observer*, the *Daily Telegraph Saturday Magazine* and the *New York Times*. He is also the author of a novel, *Unknown Pleasures* (Faber).

Hilary Davies is author of two collections, *The Shanghai Owner of the Bonzai Shop* (Enitharmon) and *In a Valley of this Restless Mind* (Enitharmon). She has also received an Eric Gregory award and first prize in the Cheltenham Literary Festival Poetry Competition. She was co-editor of *Argo*.

Philip Hensher's novels include *Kitchen Venom*, which won the Somerset Maugham Award, *Pleasured*, and *The Mulberry Empire* (Flamingo), recently long-listed for the Booker Prize.

Andy Brown's third collection of poetry, *From a Cliff*, will be published shortly by Arc. His short fiction has been anthologized in *The Gift* (NHS, edited by David Morley) . He has edited books on poetry, and co-wrote *On Science* with David Morley (Worple Press). He is currently Lecturer in Creative Writing at Exeter University.

Carol Birch has written six novels, most recently *Come Back, Paddy Riley* (Virago). Virago will publish her forthcoming untitled novel, from which 'Turn Again Home' is an extract, in 2003.

Joolz Denby has been a professional performance poet for twenty years. Her novel *Stone Baby* (HarperCollins) won the first Crimewriters' Association New Crimewriter prize. Her most recent collection of poetry and short stories is *Errors of the Spirit* (Flambard).

Lynn Kramer's short fiction and poetry have been published in magazines including *New Welsh Review* and *The Jewish Quarterly*. Macmillan has published her stories for children. She is currently working on a novel provisionally entitled *Locomotion*.

SPIKED

is a literary magazine for those interested in creative writing, cinema, photography, music and the visual arts.

Each issue includes essays, features, profiles, reviews, new fiction and poetry.

Recent issues have included Nick Hornby on film and music, W.G. Sebald and photography, Richard Holmes on biography, and reviews by Michele Roberts, George Szirtes, Ali Smith, Bridget O'Connor, and Andrew Cowen plus features on September 11 and film, the return of the Pet Shop Boys, an exile in Poland and the music of Bob Dylan.

Subscriptions (4 issues) £15 including p&p

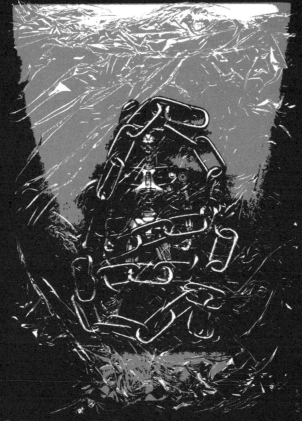

SPIKED

63 Newmarket Street Norwich NR1
www.spiked-magazine.co.uk

Submission Guidelines 2002/2003

Pen&inc is a small, independent publishing company based at the University of East Anglia. It's annual publications, *Pretext* and *Reactions*, offer the writer a place for literary experiment, and the opportunity to engage in debate about the nature of contemporary writing. Pen&inc aims to reflect the vibrant literary community within UEA, as well as the wider writing community, both national and international. Each issue is edited by a guest writer, a writer of distinction, who is invited to solicit about half of their issue, with the other half coming from the *Pretext* editorial board and unsolicited manuscripts. *Pretext* 7 (May 2003) will be guest edited by Aleksandar Hemon (*A Question of Bruno*).

Pretext Submission Guidelines

We publish short stories, poetry, essays and non-fiction, and we are looking for:

• Original short fiction (max length 6,000 words), poetry (max 5 poems), essays on writers or on writing (please submit ideas/synopses to the editors in the first instance), personal essays/memoirs.

• Please submit all work typed in a plain legible font and double-spaced with address printed on each page. Cover letter or a brief intro is fine.

• The payment is £50 for accepted publication in *Pretext*.

• Submissions should be made by post only. Faxes and emails are not accepted. Please don't send computer discs.

• Please let us know if your work is being published elsewhere during this time.

• We do not send out acknowledgement letters.

• Timing: we aim to respond in three months. However, due to the volume of work to be considered, we have unfortunately, regularly exceeded this time span, just so you are prepared for a potentially long wait. We do respond to every manuscript eventually

• Enclose SAE and postage: International Reply Coupons if you are outside the UK Please indicate (and enclose sufficient postage) if you would like your work returned, otherwise it will be recycled if unsuitable.

• Submissions for *Pretext* should be sent to: The Editor, Pretext, Pen&inc, School of English and American Studies, University of East Anglia, Norwich, Norfolk, NR4 7TJ, UK.

Deadlines for submissions to *Pretext* are end of January & end of July

REACTIONS SUBMISSION GUIDELINES

Submissions are invited from writers who have had a first collection or pamphlet published (but not a second) and from those who have not yet reached that stage. Basically, the focus is on new talent.

• Submissions must be your own original work. It can be on any subject, in any style and of any length.

• Maximum of five poems.

• Submissions should be written in English, but can be translations.

• Please submit all work typed in a plain legible font and double-spaced with address printed on each page.

• Any submission must be accompanied by a covering letter that lists the titles of your poems, plus a short biography of no more than 70 words.

• The payment is £50 for accepted publication in Reactions.

• Your submission must not have been accepted for publication in any magazine (although poems due to appear in a first collection or anthology will be considered).

• Please let us know if your work is being published elsewhere during this time.

• Submissions should be made by post only. Faxes and emails are not accepted. Please don't send computer discs.

• We do not send out acknowledgement letters.

• Timing: we aim to respond in three months. However, due to the volume of work to be considered, we have unfortunately, regularly exceeded this time span, just so you are prepared for a potentially long wait. We do respond to every manuscript eventually.

• Enclose SAE and postage: International Reply Coupons if you are outside the UK Please indicate (and enclose sufficient postage) if you would like your work returned, otherwise it will be recycled if unsuitable.

• Submissions for *Reactions* should be sent to: Esther Morgan, Pen&inc, School of English and American Studies, University of East Anglia, Norwich, Norfolk, NR4 7TJ, UK.

DEADLINE FOR SUBMISSIONS TO *REACTIONS* 4
IS: 31/03/2003

The Poetry School

in association with the Poetry Society

The Poet's Method
Lectures & Masterclasses

9 February
Lecture: Gillian Clarke

9 March
Masterclass: Don Paterson

13 April
Lecture: Marilyn Hacker

11 May
Masterclass: Bernard O'Donoghue

15 June
Lecture: Jorie Graham

The Lecture Theatre, Somerset House,
Strand, London WC2R 1LA
Sundays 3pm. Tickets £8.50, £6.50 conc.

For further details please contact
1a Jewel Rd, London E17 4QU
Tel: 020 8223 0401

email: programme@poetryschool.com

www.poetryschool.com

LONDON ARTS   The Poetry School is a limited company and registered charity No. 1069314